Geology Explained in the Lake District

By

Robert Prosser MA

Illustrated by the Author

Fineleaf Editions

CLASSIC FIELD GUIDES SERIES

Fieldwork safety
This is a reprinted edition of a classic field guide. Rock exposures described by the author may have deteriorated since the time of writing and be in a dangerous condition - particularly the mine areas: some exposures may also now be on private land, with no right of access.

Design: Philip Gray
Typeset in Adobe Garamond Pro
Print: Print Solutions Partnership and Gutenberg Press

First published by David and Charles, 1977
Published by Fineleaf Editions 2006
www.fineleaf.co.uk
Moss Cottage, Pontshill, Ross-on-Wye HR9 5TB

ISBN13: 978-0-9534437-7-2
ISBN10: 0-9534437-7-9
British Library Cataloguing in Publication Data
A catalogue record for this book is available from the British Library

Contents

Introduction to the First Edition

THE LAKE DISTRICT not only holds tremendous scenic attraction for tourists, but is also one of the most geologically rewarding regions in Britain. As such it is an area which receives a great deal of attention from visitors of all interests. There is today a growing awareness of our precious countryside heritage and how easily it can be destroyed. There is a realization too that we shall live in ever larger urban agglomerations yet have more leisure time, and probably increasing affluence – a combination which will place increasing pressure on our available open space. Conservation and enlightened development can only come from understanding, as many aspects of school curricula now acknowledge. Thus, it is hoped that books such as this will prove valuable in the nurturing of understanding.

The series to which this book belongs attempts the twin tasks of providing a stimulating and informative background to the geology and scenery of specific districts of Britain for inquiring non-specialist visitors, and presenting material appropriate for specialists wishing to undertake field investigations. Thus, this volume will present facts, the 'what' of the chosen area and also the 'why' and the 'how' behind these facts, in order to explain the results of the interactions of geology and geomorphology in the scenery of today.

The area covered by this book lies within the Lake District National Park, west of the M6, which is one of the most intensively used areas of Britain for recreation and for study (Figure 1). Geologically and scenically it is one of the most complex regions of England and within the space of this volume rigorous selection has been inevitable. The aim has been to present a series of localities which together illustrate the major geologic and scenic types of the region and thus to provide a platform for understanding other valleys and fells.

The coming of the M6 has made the Lake District easily accessible from the urbanised regions of Lancashire and the Midlands, Birmingham being only three hours away. Penrith and Kendal remain the key access towns, and there are further motorway junctions at Shap and Tebay. Nonetheless, once off the motorway, and the few main roads, the lanes remain as 'rural' as ever.

Wherever possible in this volume the sample localities are developed so that the main points can be

Fig 1: The Region

observed from a surfaced road, and then foot transects of varying length and difficulty are outlined. For all but the main paths it is advisable to utilise the Ordnance Survey map set at 1:25,000 scale.

All who leave the roads must remember that this is upland Britain where environmental conditions can be harsh and changeable. The splendid National Park Centre on the Brockhole Estate between Kendal and Windermere has information concerning the advised code of conduct on the fells, for a bright clear day can within the hour change into a deluge or blizzard with nil visibility.

Chapter 1

Overview of the Scenery and its Evolution

THIS INITIAL CHAPTER outlines the principal types of scenery and their evolution in an attempt to gain an impression of the spatial framework of the whole region before proceeding to particular localities. Scenery is the result of the interaction of long and complicated processes which may be grouped as: (a) the nature of the surface rocks and materials; (b) structural history, ie the way they lie; (c) erosional history, ie what has happened to the rocks through the work of the agencies which can weather and erode them-water, ice, wind, heat, cold and chemical action.

ROCK TYPES

Most simply, rocks are assemblages of minerals which have been consolidated to some degree. If they are categorised according to their mode of origin then three groups emerge: sedimentary, igneous and metamorphic, each being subdivisible. Sedimentary rocks originated as sediments, that is they were laid down, either on land or beneath water and were later consolidated. The materials for these sediments may have been clastic (mechanical), eg fragments of pre-existing rocks, organic, eg plant or animal remains, or inorganic (chemical), eg evaporites. In reality, many individual rock specimens are composed of a mixture of materials, eg a sandstone composed principally of clastic fragments such as shiny quartz grains may also contain plant or animal remains as fossils within the clastic matrix.

The materials for igneous rocks originate in large reservoirs of liquid material (magma) maintained at great heat and pressure within the upper mantle of the earth. Should weaknesses occur in the earth's crust then this magma is able to force its way through the crust, to cool and solidify. Should the cooling and solidification processes take place within the crust the resultant rock is known as intrusive, whereas if the magma is spilled on to the earth's surface then the rock is known as extrusive. An important subgroup are the pyroclastic rocks. These are composed of igneous materials deposited in the solid state as the emissions of explosive eruptions which shot boulders, ash and dust into the air to fall back to earth as beds which are, strictly speaking, clastic sediments of igneous material.

The word 'metamorphic' means 'changed' and metamorphic

rocks are those which have been changed from their original form by the application of heat and/or pressure normally over considerable periods of time. Any sedimentary or igneous rock can be metamorphosed at some stage during its lifetime. The amount of change may be slight and known as 'low-grade' metamorphism or may be so great that complete reconstitution has taken place and it becomes difficult to discover the original character of the rock. Such transformation is called 'high-grade' metamorphism.

STRUCTURAL HISTORY

Should pressures and strains be applied to rocks, then as alternatives to or in accompaniment with metamorphism the rock masses may bend or split in order to reduce the stresses. If the rocks bend they are said to be folded; if they split they are said to be faulted. Through geological time there have been several periods of strong crustal movement when the outer layers of the earth's crust have been subject to long-continued stresses which have resulted in tilting, folding and faulting of the rock formations (see Appendix). Such tectonic activity has been of vital importance in the creation of the Lake District scenery and examples on various scales are given throughout this book.

EROSIONAL HISTORY

Geological time is subdivided according to the standardized system laid out in the Appendix. Apart from the terminology, which is not easy to learn, the key features to note are first, that the time spans involved are enormous and second, that the periods fall into three overlapping categories: times of deposition and igneous activity, when rocks are being formed; times of mountain building (orogenesis); and times of denudation, or wearing away of the landscape. The erosional history of a region is concerned with this last process, and it will become apparent that the Lake District has undergone several cycles of denudation as well as of deposition.

THE GEOLOGIC AND SCENIC FRAMEWORK

The Lake District massif is composed in essence of three main groups of Palaeozoic rocks trending WSW-ENE, into which a number of igneous intrusions have been injected. The generalised geological map (Figure 2) indicates the overall distribution of these rock groups, the widespread glacial and post-glacial superficial deposits having been omitted for the sake of clarity. The region has been subjected to three major periods of mountain building (Caledonian, Variscan and Alpine),

Fig 2: Generalised Solid Geology

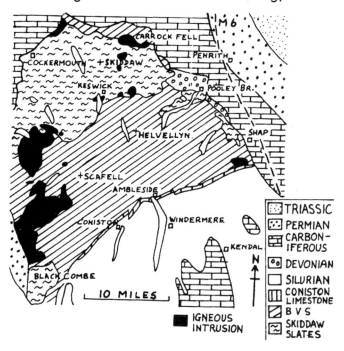

TRIASSIC
PERMIAN
CARBON-IFEROUS
DEVONIAN
SILURIAN
CONISTON LIMESTONE
BVS
SKIDDAW SLATES

IGNEOUS INTRUSION

10 MILES

N

plus recurrent faulting over long periods of time. One effect of these mighty structural movements has been to place side-by-side today, rocks which originated one above the other and many millions of years apart in time. Finally, the whole mass has been exposed to processes of erosion over millions of years until what we now see are the stumps of once great mountain masses of Himalayan dimensions.

The higher levels are usually rolling surfaces of relatively even height, which are remnants of erosion surfaces, ie surfaces produced by ancient stream systems which were working to base levels of erosion different from present sea-level. Into these ancient surfaces have been carved the great hollows and valleys radiating outwards from the central upland core. This dual landscape is illustrated by the steep scrambles up valley sides and the frequently easy walking once on the fell tops.

The three major rock groups each produce characteristic scenery. The oldest rocks, the Skiddaw Slates (Figure 2), have their main exposures north of a line from Ennerdale Water, past Derwentwater to Troutbeck and include the hill masses of the Skiddaw range and the fells around Crummock Water. The rocks are mostly dark, fine-grained, clastic sedimentary materials. There are rock crags, to be sure, but the overall scenic impression is one of relative smoothness, the rolling upper surfaces and the long fluted sides typified by the south-eastern flank of the Skiddaw block when seen from Great Mell Fell (397254).

The central Lake District is composed of immense piles of volcanic materials of the Borrowdale Volcanic Series (abbreviated to BVS throughout this book) which spread south of the Skiddaw Slate country as far as a line from Shap Fells (540090) across the northern tip of Lake Windermere to the edge of Black Combe (130850). This is wild, dark and craggy country, with extensive screes and boulder fields. The lavas, ashes and breccias with their varying jointing systems and broken structure have interacted with the weathering agencies such as water and ice to produce the most majestic scenery of the Lake District – Helvellyn, Scafell (the highest point at 3,210ft), the Langdale Pikes, Coniston Old Man, Great Gable and the many other crags so beloved of climbers. Yet once on the high fells the relative flatness is found, eg the plateau of High Street above Haweswater.

The southern section of the massif is built on marine sedimentaries, younger than the previous rock groups and consisting of more than 10,000ft of grits, flags, shales and mudstones all tilted and folded by later crustal movements. The scenery is softer and lower, only the north-eastern sector between Shap and Windermere showing extensive areas above 1,000ft. The rest is quiet wooded country sinking peacefully towards Morecambe Bay, and typified by the drive from Kendal to Windermere.

Many millions of years ago a period of crustal movement domed the Lake District and on this dome there evolved a radial drainage system, like the spokes of a wheel. Today the famous lakes etch some of these persistent spokes. More recently the three main rock groups have been alternately gouged, scalloped or veneered by ice sheets and glaciers which have helped to emphasise still further the three scenic types. These can be identified as one speeds along the M6 or potters along the lanes of the Vale of Eden.

THE GEOLOGICAL EVOLUTION OF THE AREA
• *Ordovician and Silurian Periods*
The Lake District is built upon a pre-Cambrian basement but the chronology of the surface rocks begins some 500 million years ago at the opening of the Ordovician period, 500 to 440 million years BP. (BP is the standard geological abbreviation for 'before the present'.)

Throughout these 60 million years much of what is now Britain lay submerged beneath the seas of a geosynclinal trough, with landmasses to the northwest and the southeast. A geosyncline is an extensive oceanic trough whose floor steadily subsides, permitting the deposition of great thicknesses of clastic and organic sediments over perhaps millions of years. The sediments vary according to the location of deposition within the geosyncline (Figure 3). Shelf deposits originate near the trough margins, in shallow waters with plentiful sediment supplies from the neighbouring land masses. Typical rock types are coarse grits and sandstones and, where waters were clear, limestones. Slope deposits occur further into the trough and finer rocks such as coarser shales and greywackes may result. Deep deposits originate in the heart of the trough where only the finest materials will gravitate, producing shales, siltstones and mudstones. Subsidiary undulations (geanticlines) within the geosyncline may cause complications in the sequence.

Fig 3: Elements of a Geosyncline

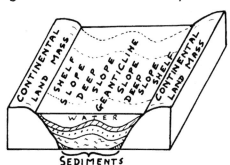

			Lake District
3	Ashgill Series ⎫	Coniston Limestone	Ashgill Shales
	⎬	Group	Applethwaite Beds
	Caradoc Series ⎭		Stockdale Rhyolite
			Stile End Beds
			Basal Conglomerate
2	Llandeilo Series	BVS	Variable succession
			and nomenclature
			according to locality
1	Llanvirn Series	Skiddaw Slates	Latterbarrow Sandstone
			Mosser-Kirkstile Slates
			Loweswater Flags

In consequence, each Ordovician locality in Britain has its individual succession and the table above is an attempt to relate the major components of the Lake District succession to the general Ordovician subdivision. (The geological convention is to place the oldest rocks at the bottom of a table, thereby simulating the actual succession.)

The Lower Ordovician period (Llanvirn Series) produced considerable thicknesses of what are mostly slope deposits of the geosyncline, black or grey marine mudstones and shales laid down in still waters. These laminar shales, whose most typical fossil is the graptolite, have suffered intense folding and have been affected by low-grade metamorphism until they are known as the Skiddaw Slates. They are irregularly cleaved and are found most extensively north of a line from Egremont and

Fig 4: Principles of Crustal Plate Tectonics

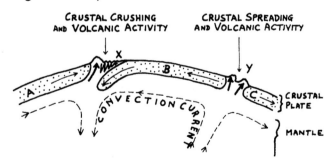

Fig 5: The Occurrence of the Ordovician Borrowdale Volcanic Series

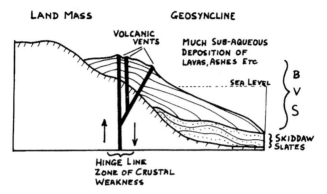

Derwentwater (Figure 2). Despite the contortion and pressures, true slates are the exception and materials of economic quality are rare. Neither the thickness nor the structures of these highly folded slates are known with accuracy although the figure of 6,000 to 7,000ft seems the best approximation.

The recent revolution in theories of the characteristics of the earth's crust suggests that the continents and oceans are underlain by massive 'plates', thousands of miles across, which move inexorably in opposing directions through geologic time, and that our earthquake and volcanic zones are found where these moving plates make contact. The mechanism for these movements is believed to

be huge, slow-moving convection currents within the earth's mantle (Figure 4). In regions where crustal plates are moving apart the crust is torn open, and where plates approach each other the crustal materials will crumple to form new mountain ranges.

In both situations zones of crustal weakness occur through which igneous materials can pass to produce periods of volcanic activity at the surface. In our study area this theory suggests that the Ordovician geosyncline was being dragged down by a downward current and that two crustal plates were moving together. Eventually, some 470 million years ago, the thousands of feet of sediments began to crumple, weaknesses appeared along the trough margins or 'hinge-line'

(Figure 5) and a spectacular volcanic episode began which produced the BVS whose remains dominate the central Lake District today. By the position of the activity in relation to the geosyncline, much of the materials would have settled and cooled subaqueously, eg Langdale district (Chapter 5).

One of the most keenly fought controversies of Lakeland geology has centred around the nature of the Skiddaw Slate/BVS junction, the crux of the argument being whether the junction is conformable or unconformable. The former is the term used when there is no chronological break in the depositional sequence, while the latter signifies a time gap between two formations. Thus, was the BVS conformable upon

Fig 6: Local Vaiations in the Borrowdale Volcanic Series

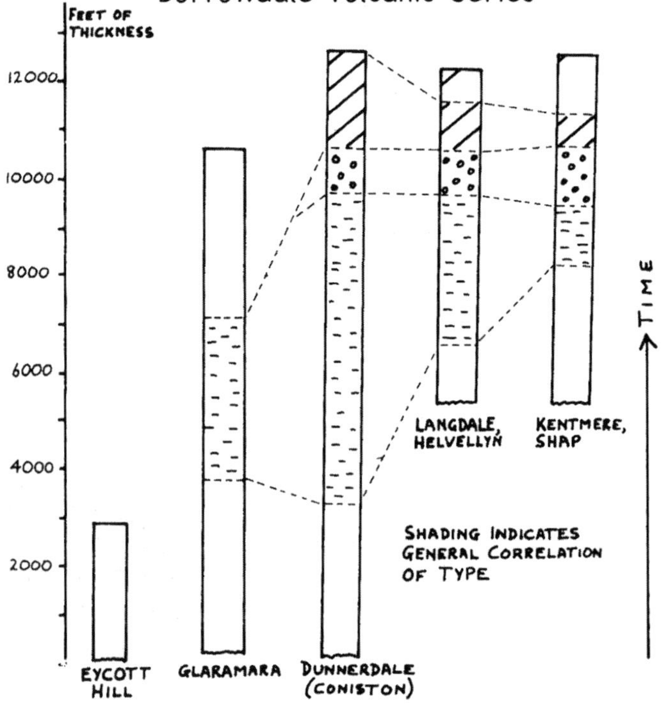

the Skiddaw Slates or was there a gap in time, ie an unconformity? A compromise proposition suggests that there is a discontinuity but that it is caused by a low-angle fault or thrust which has moved the BVS in relation to the Skiddaw Slates.

Very little is known of the vents up which the igneous materials were forced, for few have been positively identified, eg Castle Head, Keswick. The principal outlets are believed to be away to the west of the district, but lava flows and pyroclastic tuffs notoriously do not persist over horizontal distance. This lack of knowledge concerning the vents, the lateral variation in individual beds, the repetition of lavas and tuffs of very similar character at different stages in the life cycle of a particular vent, plus the structural distortion occurring since the original deposition, make the overall succession and the correlation of one locality with another exceedingly complex (Figure 6).

The maximum thickness of BVS materials mapped to date is 12,500ft along the southern limits of the main outcrop. (Hollingworth, in his guide to the Lake District National Park, puts the aggregate total as high as 20,000ft.) This is the greatest thickness of volcanic rocks of this period in Britain, being much greater than the well-known

exposures in Snowdonia. The accumulation was rapid by geologic standards and we must imagine a violent, intense holocaust of several million years. The activity was to a large degree explosive as pyroclastic tuffs, from fine dust to boulder-laden agglomerates, predominate over lavas. On the whole the mass is andesitic in character, with 50-60 per cent silica the most common proportion. This is rather surprising in the light of current research on vulcanicity which indicates that the longer the time span 'between eruptions from a particular vent (a) the more explosive the eruption and (b) the more acid, ie silica-rich, the material ejected. The former accords with the high proportion of pyroclastic materials found in the Lake District, but the latter tendency is found only in the higher, later series, which is typical of volcanic episodes where ejected materials become increasingly rhyolitic, ie acid, towards the end of a cycle of activity.

After the volcanoes became quiet, the region was uplifted and folded to a mountainous land mass which then endured several million years of erosion, ie a period of 'subaerial denudation', before the waters advanced once more and another sequence of water-lain clastic and organic sediments was deposited, ie the Coniston Limestone Group. At their base lie conglomerates, the debris of the weathered land mass, followed by a succession of shales and limestones within which were laid rhyolitic lavas and some ashes representing the death throes of the volcanic activity (the Stockdale locality, Chapter 6). Thicknesses of up to 1,100ft are exposed in a narrow belt of steeply dipping strata across the width of the Lake District from Shap, via Windermere to near Broughton. It lies unconformably upon the BVS and the Skiddaw Slates, transgressing on to progressively older beds to the west.

The waters continued to cover the area into Silurian times although the movements and long-continued sedimentation had largely filled in the basin. The 10,000-20,000ft of Silurian deposits become increasingly arenaceous flags, grits and greywackes laid down in unstable, shallow water conditions. The principal outcrops of these rocks are across the southern Lake District and the Howgill Fells. Excellent exposures can be seen in the cuttings made by the M6 as it carves its way through the Lune Gorge south of Tebay where folds and almost vertical strata show how earth movements have contorted the once-horizontal beds.

• *Devonian Period*

At the end of the Silurian period, some 400 million years ago, the mighty geosynclinal trough which had endured for more than 100 million years disappeared forever as the crustal plates finally moved together. The thousands of feet of slates, volcanic materials and later marine sediments were upthrust and contorted into mountain ranges which could be compared to the present-day Himalayas. This was the third and most severe phase of the Caledonian orogeny (mountain-building episode) and gave the familiar ENE-WSW trend lines to the Lake District and the whole of Scotland.

The earlier phases occurred first in pre-BVS times (sometimes called the pre-Bala movements) and second in Upper Ordovician times (pre-Caradoc), both of which produced folding and faulting along N-S axes. These alignments, with the ENE-WSW trend lines of the main orogeny, have been reactivated by the later Variscan and Alpine earth movements and still provide the principal tectonic directions of the region.

The gigantic 30,000ft thick sandwich of the BVS between the sedimentary series of Skiddaw Slates below and Silurian strata above, illustrate vividly the contrasting response of different rock types to tectonic stresses. The degree of strength possessed by a rock type to resist such pressures is known as its competence. The BVS are highly competent rocks and possess great resistance. Thus, they tend to form flexures rather than tight folds, resorting to faulting to release severe strains. The Skiddaw Slates on the other hand are remarkably incompetent, yielding readily to tectonic pressures which result in complex tight-fold systems. The Silurian formations are only moderately competent and again fold fairly easily.

The result of such contrasts in strength is different structural styles in each of the three major rocks groups. This has led geologists in the past to suggest that the Skiddaw Slates, for instance, were severely contorted before the occurrence of the BVS because the former are so much more intensely folded. The modern proposition states that although there was some pre-BVS upheaval, the major tectonic differences are the results of different responses to the same stresses.

Almost the whole of Britain became part of the Devonian continental land mass. Desert conditions prevailed on this continent, and where Devonian sedimentary rocks are found they are dominated by the Old Red Sandstones, eg Caithness and the Orkney Islands. Over much of Britain, however, the period was one of wearing down of the new mountain systems, including those

of the Lake District, where the Silurian and Upper Ordovician sedimentary strata were removed until in many places the Skiddaw Slates were exposed. It was this detritus which provided the material for the various Devonian sedimentaries, but in our study area the only representatives are the Mell Fell Conglomerates north of Ullswater, up to 5,000ft in thickness and lying unconformably upon the Skiddaw Slates and the BVS.

Into the roots of the Caledonian mountain chains were injected a number of igneous masses, eg the Shap Granite boss which now forms the dome of Shap Fells alongside the A6 south of Shap village, the larger Eskdale Granite, and the largely hidden Skiddaw Granite below the Caldew valley. Nothing could illustrate more clearly the extent of the wearing down of the mountains than the appearance at the surface of these and other plutonic masses, for when they were intruded some 380 million years ago they were perhaps 30,000ft below the surface.

Around each of these intrusions is a metamorphic aureole, a zone of rocks which were changed by heat, gasses and fluids emanating from the magma at the time of the injection. Such metamorphism decreases in intensity with increasing distance from the

Fig 7: The Progressive Carboniferous Inundation

A: EARLY CARBONIFEROUS

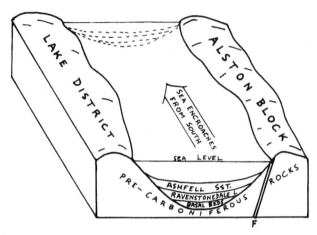

B: OPENING OF UPPER CARBONIFEROUS

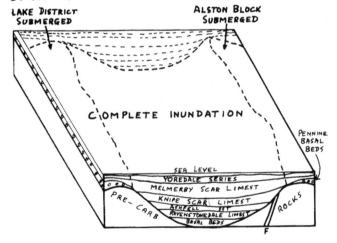

intrusive mass, although the effect may be felt up to several miles away, eg around the Skiddaw Granite boss in the north-eastern Lake District.

• *Carboniferous Period*

The Devonian period was ended some 345 million years ago by the onset of another slow but inexorable readvance of the seas over the irregular, weathered land mass which heralded the Carboniferous cycle of sedimentation. In terms of rocks and scenery one significant consequence of the gradual advance of the waters is that the complete sequence of strata is not found everywhere. These localities which were drowned first are likely to exhibit the most comprehensive succession (Figure 7).

It is believed that the seas spreading from the south eventually inundated the whole of the region, but it can only remain supposition that representative formations of the threefold subdivision of the Carboniferous-Carboniferous Limestones at the base, followed by the Millstone Grits, capped by the Coal Measures once covered the Lake District, for rocks of this age are today found only on the fringes, eg the Coal Measures of the West Cumberland Coalfield and the Carboniferous Limestones scarps crossing the A6/M6 line near Shap village.

• *Permo-Triassic Period (280-195 million years BP)*

The Carboniferous period was brought to an end by further earth movements, known as the Variscan or Hercynian orogeny, a less intense upheaval than the Caledonian movements some 120 million years earlier, but which resulted in a return to continental conditions over the whole region. The folding followed approximately the NE-SW trend of that earlier period and so the prime tectonic effect was to accentuate the Caledonian trendlines. A second effect was to resuscitate some of the generally N-S fault systems of the Lake District, lines of surface weakness which in later chapters will be seen to help control scenery in several localities.

Throughout the Permian and Triassic periods the Lake District endured continued erosion, the principal postulated effect being the progressive removal of the Carboniferous cover from the uplifted mass. Some of the eroded materials were transported eastwards into what is now the Vale of Eden which, even at this early date, was a mountain-girt basin being filled with desert sediments and later with shallow water deposits.

• *Post-Triassic Period (195-2 million years BP)*

One of the most famous and outstanding aspects of Lake

District scenery is the series of lakes and streams which radiate like the spokes of a wheel from the central highland hub, paying little attention to the pattern of rock outcrops. This drainage system has been explained as follows – after the Triassic deposition the sequence is unclear for there are no more recent solid rocks in the region. However, the supposition is that a further inundation by the seas took place in Cretaceous times, some 135 million years ago, resulting in a sedimentary succession. Once again this cycle of deposition was ended by uplift during the Alpine orogeny, in this case in the form of a broad dome upon which the radial drainage pattern evolved. The Cretaceous strata have been removed completely but the drainage pattern has been maintained on the underlying Ordovician and Silurian rocks. This is known as superimposed drainage, ie it has been superimposed from one geological pattern of outcrops on to a different underlying pattern. Other effects of the Alpine mountain building were the reactivation of the N-S fault systems.

Through the successive millions of years the predominant pattern was one of erosion towards the system of exposures we see, although there were recurrent movements along the main fault lines causing minor tectonic effects along pre-existing lines.

THE PLEISTOCENE GLACIATION

Within the past two million years ice-sheets spread themselves across Britain as far south as the western English Channel-Wash line, in what is known under the general tide of the Pleistocene Glaciation. There ware several advances and retreats and only within the last 20,000 years or so have permanent ice-fields disappeared from uplands such as the Lake District, and as recently as 9000 BC a 'mini-glaciation' produced small glaciers from the highest corries.

Four major advances and retreats have been identified, within which many local fluctuations took place, giving a very complex detailed story. Nonetheless a few generalisations may be made: as average temperatures dropped, the highlands and upland hollows formed source regions for the ice-sheets and valley glaciers which were then moved outwards by gravity and pressure flow to the lowlands. Eventually, temperature rose again, melting exceeded accumulation of snow and ice, the glacier fronts retreated and finally disappeared from their mountain hollows, leaving a vastly changed topography. In any specific locality there may be evidence of several such cycles of advance and retreat.

In glaciated landscapes we can expect to find two fundamental

Fig 8: Generalised Ice Movement from the Lake District

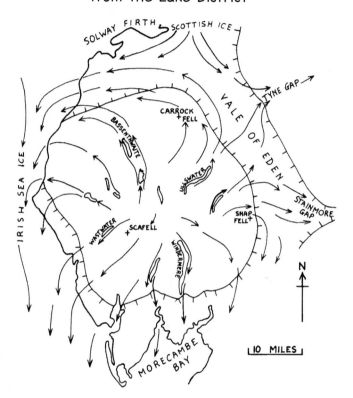

categories of feature: those produced by erosion, or wearing away, and those produced by the deposition of material. In general, the scenic effects are erosional on the highlands and depositional in the lowlands.

The principal regional ice-sheets which impinged upon the Lake District were the Scottish and Irish Sea sheets which moved in a general north-south direction around the mountain boss. These ice-sheets were prevented from

TABLE I SUMMARY OF THE EVOLUTIONARY SEQUENCE OF THE LAKE DISTRICT

Time BP (mill yrs)	Period	Events and rock types	Environment	Character
	Recent	Superficial deposits	Land mass	Erosion and deposition
2	Pleistocene	Ice Age, drift deposits	Land mass, ice-covered	Erosion and deposition
70	Post-Cretaceous	Uplift and doming Alpine orogeny	Land mass	Erosion and drainage development
135	Cretaceous	Chalk etc (supposed)	Submerged	Marine deposition
		Unconformity		Erosion
		St Bees Shales and sandstone	Land and sea	Desert land erosion; marine deposits
225	Trias	Penrith Sst and gypsum	Land mass	Desert and evaporite deposits
		Mineralisation of veins	Into land mass	Injection
280	Permian	Variscan (Hercynian) mountain building Unconformity Coal measures	Land mass	Erosion
350	Carboniferous	Millstone Grit Carboniferous Limestone	Progressive submergence	Marine deposits
		Mell Fell Conglomerates	Land mass	Storm-flood deposits in desert
400	Devonian	Igneous intrusions	Into land mass	Emplacement
		Main Caledonian mountain building Unconformity	Land mass	Erosion

440	Silurian	Silurian Grits and Flags	Submergence	Marine deposition
		Coniston Limestone Group	Submergence	Marine deposition
		Unconformity		
		Uplift: Pre-Caradoc movements	Land mass	Erosion
		BVS	Land/sea junction	Volcanic deposits
500	Ordovician	Unconformity: Pre-BVS		
		Tectonic movement		
		Skiddaw Slates	Submergence	Marine deposition

overrunning much of the Lake District by the size of the massif and by its capacity for generating its own ice cap powerful enough to support sheets and tongues flowing outwards to the surrounding lowlands (Figure 8).

At periods of maximum glaciation the ice attained thicknesses in excess of 2,000ft, thereby inundating the whole mountain mass. The sheets moved outwards until their progress was obstructed by convergence with other ice-sheets and their path turned to conform to the direction of the most powerful movement. To the west the ice flowing from the Scafell range, the Derwent Fells and the   were quickly turned southwards by the strong Irish Sea ice. On the north the ice spilling from the Skiddaw range was turned first west by convergence with the Scottish ice-sheet and then south as it contacted the Irish Sea ice.

On the east the ice from the Helvellyn range and the Shap Fells moved into the Vale of Eden and suffered a varied fate. The more northerly ice was turned northwards and westwards to squeeze across the north-western corner of the Lake District, around Carrock Fell. Other ice crossed the Vale and passed over the Pennines via the Alston and Tyne Gaps, while southerly ice, from the Shap district, moved south-eastwards through the Stainmore Gap. The southern ice from the Coniston and Kentmere Fells continued southwards as part of the main south-flowing ice-stream.

At periods of lower glaciation parts of the mountains were exposed as nunataks, ridges or plateau areas. The central mountain bosses, with corrie systems gouged into their sides, remained the principal ice collection areas and valley-glaciers moved outwards along all the major troughs. Where these ice-tongues spilled out on to the surrounding lowlands they were caught up in the regional ice movements as the thicker ice-sheets had been at maximum glaciation. At times when the Lake District ice supply was weak, the more powerful ice-sheets from the north were able to impinge upon the slopes and lower valleys, eg in Ennerdale the Irish Sea ice has left morainic drift mounds as far upvalley as the lake foot itself,

while in Eskdale deposits from this ice-sheet reach Eskdale Green.

The final stages of the two million years of the Pleistocene glaciation saw corrie glaciers surviving in their deeply shaded hollows, spilling forth their last small ice-tongues into the valleys below as recently as 9000 BC in a 'mini-glaciation' triggered by a temporary climatic deterioration.

Table 1 is an attempt to summarise the long and varied history in the most general terms. The scenery can be visualised as the outcome of the interaction of the different parameters, lithological, tectonic and geomorphological since the last, Cretaceous, submergence.

Fig 9: Base Level and Rejuvination

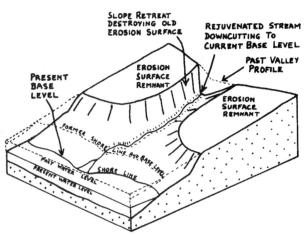

The land mass has been worked upon most persistently by stream systems. Any stream system works towards a 'base level', usually sea-level, and the form of the landscape it drains, its erosive, transportational and depositional qualities, are dependent upon this base level (Figure 9). Should sea-level fall in relation to the land, then the rejuvenated stream system will begin to erode and deposit in an attempt to come to a state of balance or 'grade' with this new base level. The work that any stream does in relation to a particular base level is part of a cycle of erosion and when the base level changes then a new cycle is begun which gradually destroys the landscape formed during the previous cycle.

The Lake District has endured a number of changes of sea-level and its topography may be thought of as a series of remnant erosion surfaces at different altitudes, separated by steeper slope sections. The oldest surfaces are the highest and usually the most fragmentary, eg the rolling plateaux of High Street are the remnants of the highest, 2,300-2,800ft erosion surface.

Chapter 2

The Skiddaw District

THE MOUNTAINS of Skiddaw (260291) and Saddleback or Blencathra (322275) are two of the best-known hill masses of the Lake District. The former towers above Keswick, the tourist focus of the northern Lake District, while the twin spurs of Saddleback watch over the traffic moving along the A594. Yet for the geologist these mountains are enigmas, hiding their complex structures beneath extensive blankets of drift, peat and scree. The Skiddaw massif is built upon Skiddaw Slates whose intensive folding is illustrated in Chapters 1 and 7. The principal fascination of this district for the geologist has centred around the two igneous sequences intruded

Fig 10: Generalised Solid Geology of the Skiddaw District

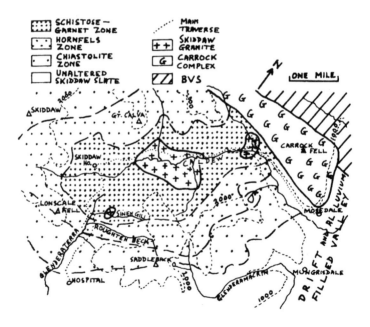

Fig 11: Schematic Impression of the South Face of the Saddleback Range

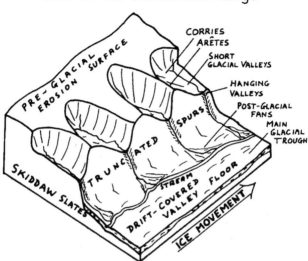

into the Ordovician mass: the Skiddaw Granite and the Carrock Fell complex (Figure 10), and in particular the fine example of a metamorphic aureole which has resulted from the emplacement of the granite mass.

No roads penetrate the massif and so foot routes are described. The basic transect (Figure 10) runs from Blencathra Hospital (303255) to Mosedale (357322) and brings together two of the classic traverses of Lake District geology. The first is the Glenderaterra path across the metamorphic aureole to the granite. The second is the Caldew valley route, again across the aureole, to the granite, with minor digressions to the Carrock Fell gabbros and the Grainsgill wolfram mine. We follow the arc from Glenderaterra in the southwest to Mosedale in the northeast, but obviously the ground can be covered from either end as two separate shorter walks. Nowhere on the main traverse are the gradients difficult although the central localities have much rough and boggy country. The highly individual scenery of is also described later in the chapter.

GLENDERATERRA TRANSECT

From the road at Threlkeld village (320253) there is a fine view of the truncated spurs of the southern face of the Saddleback range (Figure 11). This indicates the powerful ice-stream which moved eastwards leaving the heavy drift veneer of the Glenderamackin-Greta valley. Blencathra Hospital climbs the lower slopes of Blease Fell and there is a small space for parking cars at the road end (305255). A path continues around the shoulder and a small quarry immediately above the hospital typifies the features of the unaltered Skiddaw Slates (303256). These are dark-blue fine-grained Mosser Slates, rather brittle and fissile, hardened only by regional metamorphism to produce

the close-set irregular cleavage. The beds have been broken into large blocks by joint systems and the dip-strike relationships are well seen. The combination of the fractures, cleavage and bedding assist fragmentation and the rubble below the outcrop is a micro-example of the voluminous screes to be seen later below Lonscale Fell.

In the drift overlying the slates are blocks of BVS, suggesting that ice from Helvellyn range to the south pushed at least this far on to the Skiddaw massif, telling us that the Skiddaw ice was much the weaker.

From the shoulder of Blease Fell excellent views to the south illustrate some interesting relationships between structure, geomorphology and topography

Fig 12: Threlkeld Microgranite Intrusion

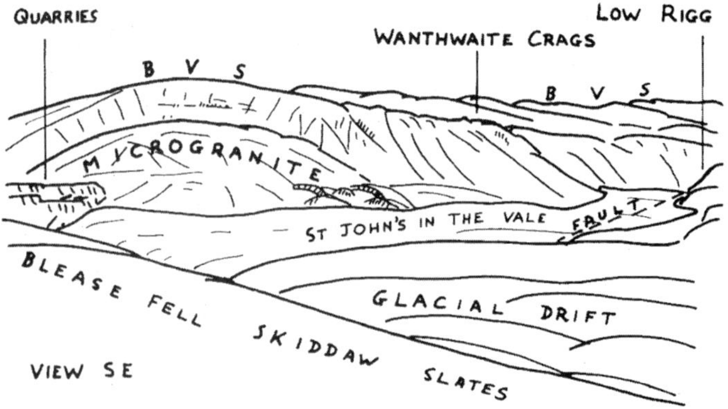

(Figure 12). To the south-east the shape of the Threlkeld Microgranite injected into the BVS can be seen by the distinctive rough dome shape above the quarries. This is a simple laccolith which has arched the beds of the overlying BVS although the metamorphic aureole is narrow. The major fault which runs almost N-S along St John's Vale through to Thirlmere defines the eastern face of Low and High Rigg (309217). This, with associated shatter belt, is one of the main dislocations of the Lake District, being traceable in the landscape from south of Skelwith Bridge (344035), north through Grasmere and Thirlmere, along Glenderaterra and west of Great Calva (290311).

The tuff and lava succession of High Rigg shows its easterly dip, giving a typically craggy topography; while Low Rigg is a second exposure of Threlkeld Microgranite. The Skiddaw Slate/BVS junction is drift-obscured, but runs along the north side of the Greta valley before cutting south-westwards beyond Brigham (280239), south of Castle Head and thence southwards along Derwentwater. Even from afar the contrast between the BVS crags of Castlerigg Fell (285197) east of the lake and the smoothed flanks of Cat Bells (244199), developed on Skiddaw Slates west of the lake, is again evident.

The Glenderaterra valley falls into three sections: a lower small basin of terraces and river bluffs around Derwentfolds Farm (298255); a gorge section defined by the main fault as far upstream as the small coniferous plantation (297268) beyond which the valley widens into an upper basin. The gorge is puzzling in that its shape suggests an absence of glaciation. The distinct V-shape is being accentuated by the stream and by the active screes of Skiddaw Slate, particularly on the shaded west flank down which fault-guided gullies plunge. However, there is an appreciable plastering of material along the eastern flank, observable below the upper path, which seems to be lateral moraine over which has crept some scree and solifluction material. The likelihood is that a small ice-tongue did move down the valley but that post-glacial processes have modified the effects. Any such ice movement down the Glenderaterra valley would have been further hampered by the pressure of ice from the south noted earlier.

The upper basin has the typical features of a névé collection bowl – the wide collection area, the mantle of drift producing marshy country today. In addition, an incipient corrie hollow has developed on the northern flanks of Lonscale Fell.

Fig 13: Skiddaw Granite Outcrops

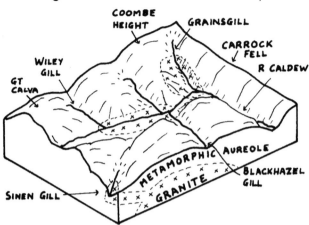

The principal axis of the Skiddaw Slate anticlinorium, trending WSW-ENE, passes north of Lonscale Fell, across the Glenderaterra valley. The complex folding, the long erosional history and the heavy scree and drift veneer make this feature difficult to follow in the field although the overall orientation of the exposures on the upper crags of Lonscale Fell suggest a southerly dip. Eastwards, across the Caldew valley and Carrock Fell, the trend curves W-E then WNW-ESE. Into this anticlinorium was injected, late in the Devonian period, the Skiddaw Granite laccolith (Figure 13). The walk up the Glenderaterra valley is basically an approach to this intrusion across the metamorphic aureole. Intensity of metamorphism increases upvalley and although a wide variety of rock types may be found, three major zones are commonly identified. Figure 10 shows the three zones surrounding the intrusion and how the transect takes in the full sequence.

The small quarry above the hospital has illustrated the unaltered slates, developed from argillaceous sediments. Following the path the first change is noticeable on a rocky outcrop at about 400 yards (299259) where the slate has been hardened and tiny white flakes of mica can be seen. The hardening of rocks such as the Skiddaw Slates by metamorphism is, in essence, the removal of water from the crystal lattice to produce a heavier more compact rock. This is within the so-called chiastolite zone, although at this location the chiastolite is not evident. A little further upvalley, where a gill running from Blease Fell crosses the path (300269), perfect examples of chiastolite slates are exposed. The dark-grey mudstones have been hardened and cleaved, and contain the slender silver needles of chiastolite up to 1 inch long. This is a form of aluminium silicate, with a diamond-shaped cross-section with a black spot in the centre (Figure 14). This dark centre and the overall opaqueness distinguish it from the chemically similar andalusite, which is brighter and to be found more abundantly further within the aureole.

A second feature of this location is an excellent shatter zone associated with a fault. The closely set, near-vertical joints have permitted the long-continued percolation of haematite-rich water until there is considerable reddening of the rocks. This is not simply surface staining but a deep impregnation of the materials.

Continuing to Roughten Gill (298276), the intensification of the metamorphism is indicated by an increasing rotation and alignment of the chiastolite needles and the appearance of the so-called 'spotted-slates'. The grey rock was originally coarser in grain, perhaps a sandy mudstone, and part of the arenaceous facies of the Skiddaw Slates. The spotting is caused

Fig 14: Chiastolite Slate

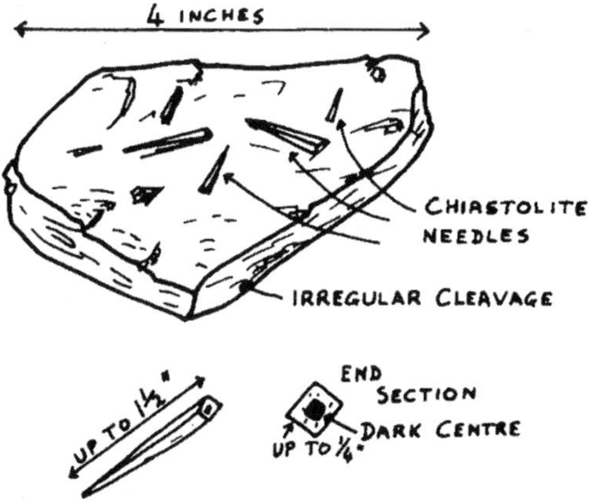

4 INCHES

CHIASTOLITE NEEDLES

IRREGULAR CLEAVAGE

END SECTION
DARK CENTRE

UP TO 1¼"

UP TO ⅛"

by iron sulphide which tends to agglomerate under conditions of considerable heat, and the rock is approaching a cordierite-hornfels, as we are now in the hornfels zone of the aureole.

Amid the boulders in this stream, sub-angular blocks of black and white Skiddaw Granite are found, indicating an exposure upstream. Also in the debris, some Skiddaw Slate blocks reveal examples of micro-folding, with amplitudes of a few inches, illustrating the detailed contortion to which these Lower Ordovician sediments have been subjected.

The next beck crossed is Sinen Gill (297278). If the stream is followed towards its source, pale granite boulders become more frequent, and, dependent upon the erosion-deposition balance, patches of granite may be seen in situ. In the stream banks some examples of rotted granite peep out, resembling crumbly kaolinite, the result of chemical action from percolating acid ground water from the overlying peat. The traditional exposure of the igneous rock is, however, at the waterfall (301282) where the stream rumbles over the massive blocks opened up by the rectangular jointing system. Above the falls, fresh-swept granite is seen for at least 25 yards and then continues in the north bank. Careful attention to this outcrop will reveal that the texture becomes increasingly fine-grained upstream. This replaces the cordierite-hornfels, a massive, dark, flinty rock twinkling with white mica flakes and red garnets. In this innermost schistose-garnet zone of the aureole both bedding and cleavage are generally absent. The banding seen on weathered surfaces is the result of differential hardness. The progression of metamorphism from Roughten Gill has been through an increasingly ferro-magnesian-rich zone, eg where augite is common, to an innermost schistose zone where garnets appear and andalusite is common.

THE SKIDDAW GRANITE

The Skiddaw Granite is a simple laccolith from which two eminences or apophyses have been thrust. The intrusion occurred parallel to and within the heart of the main axis of the anticlinorium, being injected in late Devonian times. Despite the splendid and extensive metamorphic aureole indicating the presence of the granite not far below the surface, exposures of this igneous rock are restricted to three localities (Figure 13): Sinen Gill in the south-west, the central Caldew basin and the Caldew-Grainsgill in the north-west.

All three exposures are different in detail, but all do reveal the 'normal' granite, a grey coarse-grained rock of quartz, felspars and dark biotite mica plus small quantities of white muscovite mica. Phenocrysts of white perthite felspar are common and up to 2 inches in length, while the biotite sometimes varies from its usual black to a brown-red tinge. The larger crystals are usually the felspars, while the quartz occurs as irregular shiny fragments and the mica as small glittering pieces.

The small Sinen Gill exposure consists of a granite which is more basic than elsewhere, the biotite in particular being more abundant. Phenocrysts of felspar occur irregularly. The junction with the country rock dips northwards at approximately 20° while the country rocks themselves are contorted but in general dip southwards at generally high angles.

The central outcrop, although the largest of the three and covering half a square mile, is generally masked with drift and exposures are restricted to stream beds and banks, eg Wiley Gill (303305) and Blackhazel Beck (315309). It is again grey, but a rather more acid granite with less biotite and few phenocrysts. The acidity increases generally eastwards and in the Caldew and Blackhazel Beck a pinkish to white aplitic rock can be seen, fine grained and free from biotite, but with increasing muscovite.

The north-eastern outcrop around the junction of the Caldew and Grainsgill Becks contains two distinctive rock types, although the change between the types is gradational. At the western end of the outcrop, the granite in the bed of the Caldew (325325) is normal although the most acid of the three localities. Towards Grainsgill the felspars almost disappear and a quartz-mica rock known as a greisen develops. This is frequently a pale yellow-green in colour, indicating the presence of chlorite, probably from the breakdown of certain of the felspars.

UPPER GLENDERATERRA

In the main valley the disused Glenderaterra lead mine is worth a visit (297271). It operated spasmodically during the nineteenth century and as late as 1920 but was never very productive. Despite the efforts of 'rockhounds' over the years, even a brief search of the spoil heaps will produce galena nodules, calcite crystals, witherite (a form of calcite in thin plates), the brilliant malachite (copper), chalcopyrites and barytes. The excellent fault breccias found tell us that the adits followed the N-S shatter zone of the main fault which was penetrated by the mineral-bearing solutions. The breccias show black slate fragments rimmed by a lattice of red-brown ferruginous secondary infilling.

No adits are now visible. On the bank opposite to the spoil heaps the rather massive spotted slates, with near-vertical joint systems, form a strong stream bluff. There are remnants of several other mines above and below this site, some with spoil heaps. Just above the junction of Glenderaterra stream and Roughten Gill (297275), a copper vein can be detected by the abundance of rust-stained quartz.

The upper Glenderaterra basin was once the collecting ground for snow and ice and is now heavily plastered with drift and peat, very boggy and hummocky, from the materials deposited as the ice melted in situ. The area is rather dull and certainly difficult to traverse except along the main path to Skiddaw House (288291).

CALDEW VALLEY

This section begins at Skiddaw House and ends at Mosedale village, continuing from the Glenderaterra transect. However, it is perfectly feasible to walk in the reverse direction, upvalley from Mosedale, or even from the road head at Grainsgill Bridge (325329). Whichever direction is taken the path is well marked and the gradient easy.

From Skiddaw House the path rolls north-eastwards into the basin directly towards the dark long mass of Carrock Fell across heavy boulder clay. The heart of the basin is underlain by the central outcrop of the Skiddaw Granite while to the right the smoothed flanks of Saddleback rise away, hiding the crags and corries of the south-east face. The dips of the slates are generally to the south and vary widely from 20° to 70°. To the left rise the twin hills of Great Calva (291311) and Coomb Height (310328). Great Calva is built of hardened spotted slates and is isolated by faults to west and east. The former is seemingly the continuation of the Glenderaterra shatter belt although the drift makes identification difficult. Coomb Height is composed of Skiddaw Granite with a metamorphosed Skiddaw Slate capping, this representing a fragment of the roof of the intrusion.

The drift and peat of the broad bleak upper Caldew basin hides the granite very effectively. The smoothed slopes are broken only by the crags and screes of Lonscale Fell. The variability of the drift veneer can be seen as the path crosses Wiley Gill where non-porphyritic granite is exposed in the stream bank (Figure 15). Above, the drift is in places barely a foot thick, the sandy matrix containing fragments and boulders of granite and metamorphosed slate up to two feet in diameter,

Fig 15: Skiddaw Granite Exposed in Wiley Gill

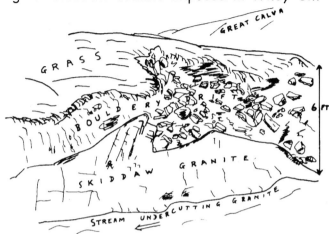

clearly local in origin. The solid granite in the stream bank shows much iron staining.

Eastwards the path continues across the bouldery drift, the slope above showing occasional outcrops of the schistose hornfels of the inner aureole. At the flat floor of the amphitheatre there are appreciable alluvial patches. At the eastern end of the granite outcrop, where a beck enters the north bank of the Caldew (313313), some good exposures of grey-green spotted slates con-taining much andalusite can be followed. In the Caldew itself and up the Blackhazel Beck, the pink aplitic variety of the granite is seen, while in the latter beck the junction with the slates can be located (318306) followed by some exposures of the mica schist, the cordierite-hornfels sequence, until the return of the cleavage developed in the grey flags and grits.

As we follow the Caldew downstream from this point along the steadily widening valley, we are following the metamorphic aureole outwards, that is in reverse order from the ascent of Glenderaterra. As far as Grainsgill Bridge we remain within the schistose-garnet zone, although the most common rocks exposed in the stream bed are dark cordierite-hornfels with andalusite. The boulder clays over which the track runs contain many examples of the chiastolite slates and spotted slates. In the stream

Fig 16: Grainsgill - Skiddaw Granite-Greisen

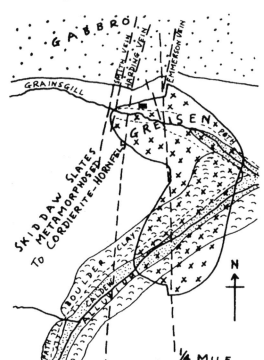

bed the metamorphosed slate-granite junction can be located at low-water periods (329326).

Grainsgill cuts through the greisen sector of the intrusion, there being a number of exposures of the pale often yellowish rock in the stream and lower flanks including the foundations of the bridge itself. The principal interest in this extension of the main intrusion is that it is crossed by faults which have permitted the development of mineralised veins (Figure 16). The three principal veins – Smith, Harding and Emmerson – run almost N-S and are nearly vertical. The quartz-mica greisen occupies the lower slopes of Grainsgill and Brandy Gill valleys and set within it, along the vein system, is a lode of lead which has been worked in the past and is the cause of much of the chaos in the valley. It is interesting to note that the veins cut into the gabbros of Carrock Fell, thereby telling us that they are younger than that intrusive complex.

The ore veins are offshoots from the Skiddaw Granite and are typical in that they contain a variety of minerals, the result of a sequence of crystallisation from chemicalised gases and solutions in the process known as pneumatolysis. The emanations also help in the formation of the greisen by removing the felspars, replacing them by micas and leaving the quartz-mica rock. The veins are generally from 2ft to 4ft thick and thin out to north and south. The most important mineral gained from the numerous levels and adits forced into the veins is wolfram, the ore for tungsten. It is a heavy mineral composed of manganese and iron. Originally worked in the nineteenth century, the levels were reopened in both World Wars, and in 1972 were resuscitated by the mining of a new level 800 yards into the hill. The outcry from conservationists concerning the considerable pollution of the stream and the hillsides in this lovely part of the National Park was mounting when the operation was closed down by the autumn of 1972 (Figure 17). The Grainsgill-Brandy Gill locality is a most rewarding site for finding minerals, the vein

Fig 17: View East From Grainsgill

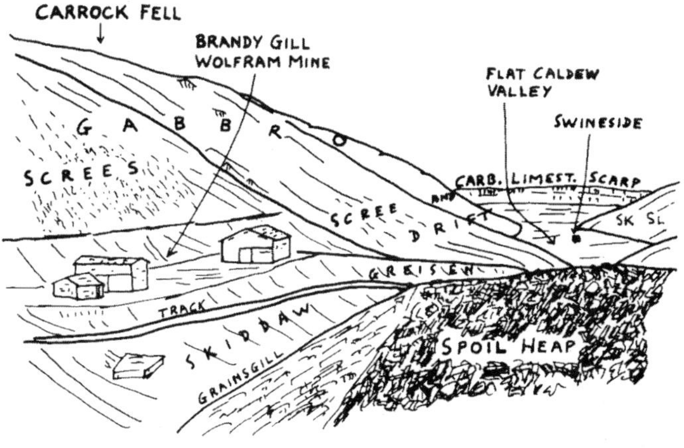

Mineral	Clues to identification
Molybdenite	Soft silvery mineral in small pliable flakes
Bismuthinite	Hard, silvery grey but less bright than molybdenite
Wolfram	Heavy, black, shiny mineral, usually as blade-like form in white quartz
Scheelite	Heavy, yellow resinous-looking mineral, perhaps as glassy four-sided pyramids
Apatite	Pale-green prisms on quartz, up to one inch long
Mispickel (arsenical pyrites)	Hard tin-white when fresh; tarnishes to yellow and browns, and often occurs in tabular crystals
Tourmaline	Greeny-black mineral as long shiny needles

(Description after Shackleton, E. H. Lakeland Geology 3rd edition (Dalesman 1971).

systems yielding a wider range than elsewhere in the Lake District. This is one of Shackleton's favourite spots and the following list uses his lucid descriptions of the principal minerals to be found.

From Grainsgill Bridge to Mosedale the Caldew develops a broad flat valley, up to 300 yards across, with alluvial terraces as far as Swineside (339323) and then a low-lying alluvial flat, although the stream remains a fine boulder-strewn mountain beck. The smooth slopes of Bowscale Fell on the south, into which the corrie hollow of Bowscale Tarn has been cut, contrast with the knobbly scree-strewn slopes of Carrock Fell with its greys, blacks and blues. The Carrock Fell flank is deeply covered in screes, including some fine stone chutes and fans. These are of angular boulders up to 3 feet across and small stones, best exposed where cut by gullies. The rubble includes the heavy dark gabbro, pink or grey granophyre and occasional speckled diorite, illustrating the range of rock types on Carrock Fell. The lower slopes astride the road are plastered with boulder clays (Figure 18).

The journey down the valley follows the sequence of decreasing metamorphism. Below the bridge the greisen-metamorphised slate junction can be seen in the Caldew bed. The very pale greisen gives way to a quartz-rich rock in which garnets are abundant and the biotite has been converted to green chloritic material. In the valley floor immediately west of

Fig 18: Slope Facets in the Caldew Valley

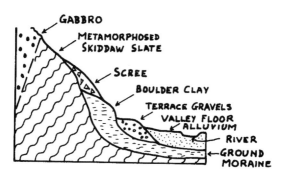

Swineside some small glaciated bosses of metamorphic rock are deep brown in colour with quartz, felspars, biotite and muscovite, plus a few cordierite crystals.

However, their most distinctive feature is the micro-folding shown on weathered faces. These folds are often extremely angular and isoclinal.

Fig 19: Landscape Elements Around Mosedale

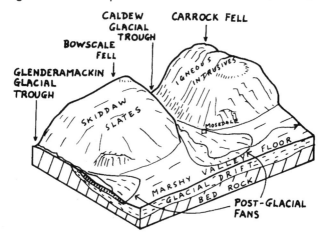

Fig 20: Geology of Carrock Fell

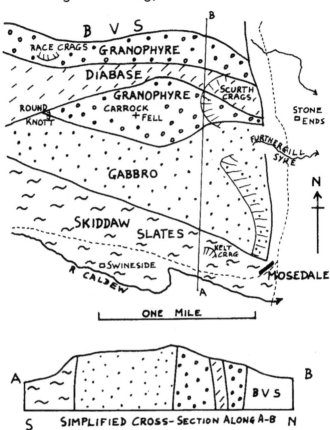

SIMPLIFIED CROSS-SECTION ALONG A-B

Below Swineside the broad flat floor of the Caldew valley has been built up of the copious material, often coarse in nature, laid down by the stream from late glacial times. The huge volume of this material is illustrated further by the extensive alluvial fan which has spilled out on top of the glacial drift in the depression east of Mosedale (Figure 19). A similar fan has been developed by the Glenderamackin and both are easily distinguishable from the drift by being less boggy and better cultivated.

CARROCK FELL

This famous cigar-shaped hill is a complex mass of igneous intrusions yielding a wide range of rock types (Figure 20). It is only possible to give here a mere glimpse of its character at its eastern end. The junction of the metamorphosed Skiddaw Slates with the intrusive gabbros of Carrock Fell can be followed from Mosedale to the Brandy Gill Mine, running parallel to and above the road. The nature of this junction has always aroused dispute and it is still not certain whether or not it is a fault junction.

If one strikes upslope immediately behind Mosedale village towards Kelt Crag, then above the boulder clay are highly contorted Loweswater Flags, at first not highly metamorphosed. Over the next 50 yards the slates become increasingly hardened until garnets appear. Bedding disappears and finally the crystalline rocks give way some 30 yards later to a dark, heavy, biotite-rich ilmenite gabbro. Although there are porphyroblasts at the junction and signs of metasomatism, the contact zone is only some 3 yards wide. There is no shatter zone and so the question still remains – is it a fault junction?

The Carrock Fell mass is composed of a series of steeply dipping sheets and lenses of igneous intrusive rocks, dipping to the north and striking W-E and WNW-ESE, resulting in the successive outcrops of gabbros, granophyre, diorite and felsite, the suite ending abruptly on the east. The intrusions seem to be Devonian in age and have been emplaced parallel to the strike of the main Caledonian folding along the Skiddaw Slate-BVS junction.

Upslope from the slate-gabbro junction the rock is at first the heavy variety, very dark, with shining black grains of magnetite and the less-conspicuous ilmenite. The gabbro becomes less heavy and lighter in colour with some large pale felspar crystals before an abrupt change to granophyre near the summit. This is much more acidic, composed of quartz and felspars, a pink and grey rock of medium texture. Identification in the scenery is facilitated by the small material in the granophyre screes, in contrast to the massive blocks so common in the gabbro rock piles. Beyond the summit with its hill fort (341337) the lens of granophyre is succeeded by a sheet of diorite (diabase), a dark-green fine-grained rock with abundant hornblende.

The summit gives fine views to the east and southeast and three features in particular are worth noting. First the wide marshy trough of the Caldew and Glenderamackin, underlain by Skiddaw Slates but veneered with boulder clay and lacustrine deposits from a late-glacial lake. These, in turn, are overlain by the better drained alluvial and gravel fans of the two rivers where they spill out from their hill-girt troughs. Second, the forested Greystoke Park, due east, sits on top of the west-facing Carboniferous Limestone

Fig 21: Generalised Geology – Eycott Hill

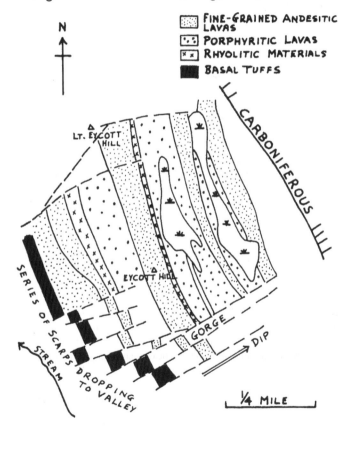

N

FINE-GRAINED ANDESITIC LAVAS
PORPHYRITIC LAVAS
RHYOLITIC MATERIALS
BASAL TUFFS

CARBONIFEROUS

LT. EYCOTT HILL

EYCOTT HILL

SERIES OF SCARPS DROPPING TO VALLEY

STREAM

GORGE

DIP

¼ MILE

Fig 22: Highly Simplified Impression of the Eycott Hill Structure

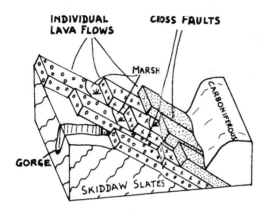

scarp which runs NNW-SSE past Hutton Roof (373341). Third, to the southeast immediately in front of this scarp, is an area of broken landscape. These are the famous Eycott Hill exposures (387295), a detached extension of the BVS exhibiting a wide range of basic and acid lava flows stretching two miles NNW-SSE (Figure 21). They dip at approximately 40° to the east but the irregularity of the broken, west-facing scarps indicate the complex fault systems which have fragmented the mass (Figure 22).

Carrock Fell summit gives an overview of the Skiddaw Massif with the Skiddaw Granite intrusion and its aureole and provides a location from which to ponder the question: Why is it that the Skiddaw Granite, itself a resistant rock, and the hardened metamorphic rocks of the inner aureole have produced a basin surrounded by hill masses largely of rocks which are logically less resistant to the agencies of erosion?

The most easily accessible gabbro exposures are seen in the roadside rock face immediately north of Mosedale village (356324). The first rocks are the knobbly, black, heavy marginal gabbro, followed to the north by the 'normal' variety. By the time Stone Ends (355335) is reached the light-coloured granophyre is seen in the debris along the rock face.

Chapter 3

Facets of Borrowdale

THIS CHAPTER is so titled because Borrowdale is a large complex valley and all that is attempted here is an overview, with some detailed glimpses of its varied character. With Windermere it is the most frequently visited Lake District valley, being directly accessible from Keswick. The complete valley includes the broad basin which contains the lakes of Bassenthwaite and Derwentwater, this basin being pinched out upvalley by the fine gorge section known as The Jaws of Borrowdale (252167). Above the gorge an upper basin opens up into which gather the Seathwaite and Stonethwaite troughs (Figure 23).

The valley is particularly interesting for two aspects of its formation. First, the junction of the Skiddaw Slates with the overlying BVS and the contrasting scenery developed on these rock groups; second, the highly varied topography and distinctive features produced by the Pleistocene glaciation. The district lies on the southern end of the Scafell synclinorium (Chapter 1), each fold trending generally WSW-ENE and pitching to the east. Towards the core of the anticlinorium the highly folded Skiddaw Slates outcrop from Derwentwater northwards, the

approximate junction with the BVS being shown on Figure 23.

The BVS dip to the ESE along the eastern flank of Derwentwater, but the dip swings steadily to the south across the upper trough. Although these 10,000ft and more of volcanic lavas, tuffs and agglomerates are far less contorted than the Skiddaw Slates, the character of the flexures in the overall dip structure is illustrated by the cross-sections of Figure 24 along the crags and fells east of the main valley, providing an excellent example of the different structural styles in rocks of contrasting competence.

From the ice-collection fields of the knot of mountains spreading out from Great Gable (211103), at maximum glaciation an ice sheet moved northward across the whole district. Later, vigorous ice-streams moved down these valleys, joining and gaining size until they spilled out to the Cumberland Plain beyond Bassenthwaite.

DERWENTWATER BASIN

A useful starting point is Castle Head (270228), the first wooded knoll south of Keswick. Climbing from the road to the summit one emerges from the trees to stand on solid rock, a hard, dark, fine-grained dolerite with the glittering

Fig 23: Borrowdale

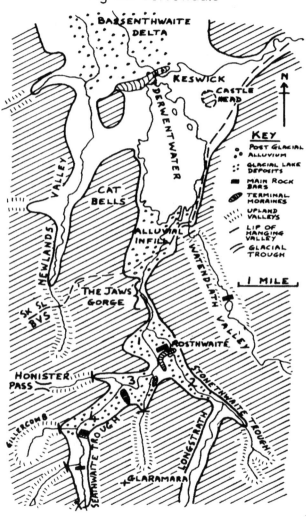

KEY

- •• POST GLACIAL ALLUVIUM
- ∴ GLACIAL LAKE DEPOSITS
- ▬ MAIN ROCK BARS
- ⬭ TERMINAL MORAINES
- ⠇⠇⠇ UPLAND VALLEYS
- ⌣ LIP OF HANGING VALLEY
- ⫽⫽ GLACIAL TROUGH

1 MILE

BASSENTHWAITE DELTA

KESWICK

CASTLE HEAD

N

DERWENTWATER

VALLEY

CAT BELLS

ALLUVIAL INFILL

NEWLANDS

WATENDLATH VALLEY

THE JAWS GORGE

SK SL BVS

ROSTHWAITE

HONISTER PASS

STONETHWAITE TROUGH

GILLERCOMB

SEATHWAITE TROUGH

LONGSTRATH

STONETHWAITE TROUGH

GLARAMARA

augite identifiable. Looking south the crags of Walla Crag (278213) glower back above the shirt front of Great Wood. The soft topography surrounding the Castle Head eminence is built on drift-covered Skiddaw Slate (Figure 25), while Walla Crags are a series of massive lava flows of the Lower Andesites, interspersed with tuff beds, dipping away from the observer. The usually accepted relationship between the dolerite and the andesites is that Castle Head represents the former volcanic vent for the igneous materials which were ejected to form a volcano (the

remnants of which are now seen in Walla Crag), leaving Castle Head as the stump of a volcanic plug or 'neck'. Such a proposition tells us of the considerable thickness of tough igneous beds which have been removed to produce such relict features. One of the problems of accepting such a straightforward answer to the Castle Head dolerite is that there seems to be minimal effect on the surrounding Skiddaw Slate.

The Skiddaw Slate-BVS junction is largely masked with drift, but Shackleton's classic transect of Cat Ghyll includes a junction

Fig 24: Simplified Geology of the East Flank of Borrowdale

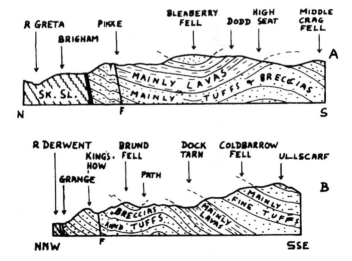

Fig 25: Supposed Castle Head–Walla Crag Relationship

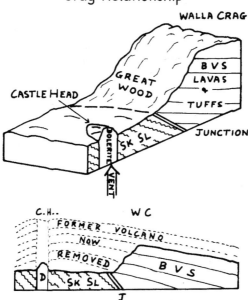

observable in a small cave beside the lake some 120 yards north of the Ghyll (269211) where hard slates are seen in contact with a breccia. This famous transect up Cat Ghyll, first published in the Geological Memoir (1876) and since followed by Shackleton in beautiful detail, is not laid out in this volume as it is so readily available and also because it is a strenuous scramble for the specialist. It illustrates the local dominance of lavas overlying a coarse breccia base and returning eventually to breccias and tuffs near the summit of Bleaberry Fell (285197). The basal purple breccias are easily seen at Cat Ghyll beside the road (270210), and they represent the early explosive stage of the volcano when fragments of both igneous and pre-existing country rock, ie Skiddaw Slates, were blasted into the air, the coarser material falling immediately around the vent and the finer materials being deposited over a greater distance. Bedding observable in ash bands as well as cooling features in the lavas suggest that this series was laid down below water.

Taking a broader prospect from Castle Head there is a good view to the north across the large terminal moraine behind which the shallow lake of Derwentwater has been impounded, although it was formerly joined to Bassenthwaite. The flat expanse of the Bassenthwaite delta has been formed within the past 12,000 years with material brought down from the surrounding mountains by the several streams which spill into this section of the basin. Like the Buttermere delta (Chapter 7), the rock floor is here not deep but the extent of the delta shows the enormous transportation capacity of the streams, particularly in the snow-melt and flood seasons of the immediately post-glacial period.

The outlook to the west is dominated by the high but smooth Skiddaw Slate mountains of the Thornthwaite and Derwent Fells, great thicknesses of mudstones, shales and flags complexly folded (Chapter 7). Perhaps the most distinctive topographic feature is the almost complete destruction of the pre-glacial erosion surfaces by slope retreat of the deeply incised valleys. Such retreat, aided by ice moving over the flanks,

has produced the smooth cigar-shaped ridges exemplified best by Cat Bells (245199). Swineside (243225) marks a further stage in the reduction of hill masses – the isolated smoothed hill, in this case barely 800ft high. In contrast, a glance southwards along the eastern flank of Derwentwater yields a series of tumbling crags leading to the Jaws beyond the lake. This is a preview of the BVS scenery to be walked later in this chapter.

From Castle Head the road (B5289) passes beneath the towering crags of Walla and Falcon Crags from which huge blocks have been prised by mechanical erosion processes to become part of rock slopes only partially stabilised by vegetation. The junction between the Skiddaw Slates and the BVS runs along and immediately below the road.

The upper portion of the Derwentwater basin is best seen from the bluffs above the Ashness Bridge car park (269199) where one stands on top of individual beds of hard ashes dipping away from the lake, leaving their ice-plucked scarps towering vertically above the lake.

From the cliff top the extensive post-glacial infilling of the Derwentwater basin is evident in the flat and often marshy terrain below Grange village (252175). Especially worthy of note is the fine delta which is being actively extended into the lake, exhibiting some of the typical features of a bird's foot delta. Sedimentation takes place along the bed and banks of the main channel, and its mouth. This sedimentation is caused by friction which decreases the ability of the stream to transport its load – friction which affects especially the laden water immediately adjacent to the bed and sides, which are aggraded in consequence. Similar loss of capacity occurs at the mouth of the channel where the water enters the lake and once more deposition takes place, eg note the brown coloration denoting very shallow water beyond the mouth of the delta. As a channel becomes clogged with sediment a new outlet may be opened up by a flood surge, leaving the old channel abandoned after which it is slowly aggraded with the aid of water plants whose roots and foliage capture further fine sediment. Finally the area may be raised above lake-level.

Along the eastern flank of the lake to the south, further BVS tuffs

Fig 26: The BVS-Skiddaw Slate Junction at Hollows Farm

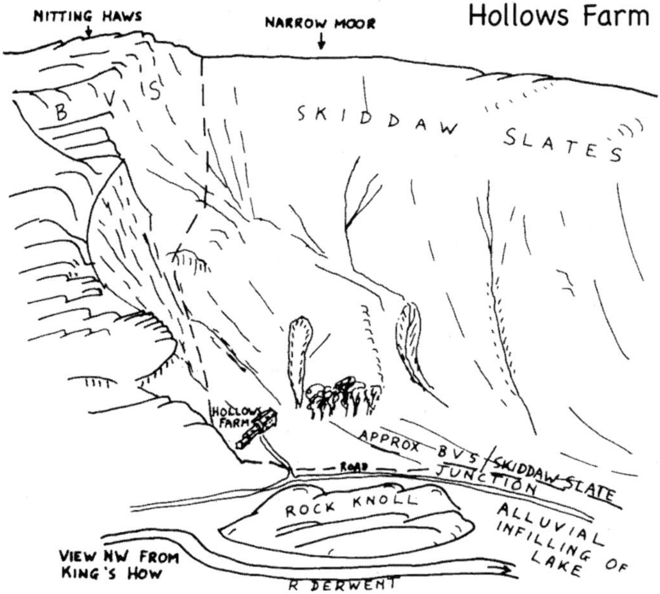

NITTING HAWS

NARROW MOOR

B V S

SKIDDAW SLATES

HOLLOWS FARM

APPROX BVS/SKIDDAW SLATE JUNCTION

— ROAD —

ROCK KNOLL

ALLUVIAL INFILLING OF LAKE

VIEW NW FROM KING'S HOW

R DERWENT

and lava flows form the brows of Gowder Crag (268186), Brown Dodd (266178) and Kings How (258167), their scarps jutting above the valley, while from between them spills the Watendlath Beck at Lodore Cascade (265188) - our first example of Borrowdale's hanging valleys. By the time the knob of King's How is reached, the basin has narrowed to a gorge and BVS crags now appear on the western flank at Low Scawdel and Castle Crag (249159). This is the famous gorge of The Jaws of Borrowdale where particularly hardened beds of igneous materials have resisted even the immense power of the ice.

Looking northwards along the western flank of the valley from Castle Crag the knobs and scars of the BVS continue across Low Scawdel, but above Grange village there is a distinct change of surface character, the slopes becoming smooth with few outcrops across Narrow Moor (Figure 26). This is the classic Hollows Farm (now a Youth Hostel) junction of the Skiddaw Slates and BVS, the junction having crossed the valley above Grange.

The junction can be examined from Grange village. Part of the village stands upon a magnificent roche moutonnée – an ice-smoothed and grooved rock. The striations or scratches scored by rock fragments held in the sole of the glacier point

downvalley in the direction of ice movement. From the village walk south west to Hollows Farm (248171) and climb directly upslope behind the buildings, following the line of the sike. At first the small outcrops are of Skiddaw Slate but after a break of slope keep to the crags on the left, and there, beneath the oft-visited holly bush clinging to the rock, the junction will be found. The dark BVS tuffs have weathered to a white patina while the Skiddaw Slates are of a brown colour. This junction marks the onset of the Ordovician volcanic cataclysm following the millions of years of quiet sedimentation in the geosynclinal waters. This is one of the junctions which appear conformable but opinion is now swinging towards a discontinuity between the Skiddaw Slates and the BVS. Comparison of this junction with that of the Buttermere junction below Fleetwith Pike (Chapter 7), at which there is a clear discontinuity, illustrates the complexity of this problem.

THE WATENDLATH VALLEY

I am reluctant to encourage more people to use the Watendlath valley - overrun as it is through much of the summer - but it is a lovely example of the smaller, upland Cumbrian valleys (Figure 27). It falls into three sections, the form of each being greatly influenced by the

Fig 27: The Watendlath Valley

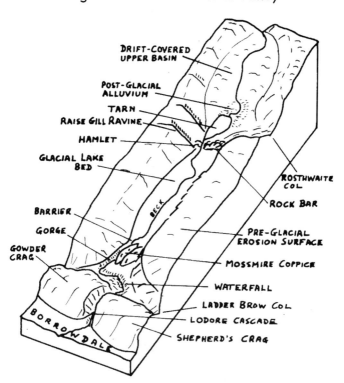

DRIFT-COVERED
UPPER BASIN

POST-GLACIAL
ALLUVIUM

TARN

RAISE GILL RAVINE

HAMLET

GLACIAL LAKE
BED

BARRIER

GORGE

GOWDER
CRAG

BORROWDALE

BECK

ROSTHWAITE
COL

ROCK BAR

PRE-GLACIAL
EROSION SURFACE

MOSSMIRE COPPICE

WATERFALL

LADDER BROW COL

LODORE CASCADE

SHEPHERD'S CRAG

action of ice and its meltwaters: an upper basin including Watendlath Tarn (275161), a middle section of a small glacial trough, and a lowermost gorge section. Side valleys such as this often possessed their own ice-collection basins set into the upland surface which provided a supply for a small ice-tongue to push downvalley and join the main stream moving down Borrowdale. The erosive power of the Watendlath valley glacier was much less than the Borrowdale ice-stream. This latter basin was overdeepened and after the disappearance of the ice-masses the Watendlath Valley was left 'hanging' high above Derwentwater.

The transect along the lane from the lakeside road (269203) to Watendlath hamlet (276163) passes upwards through a thick and variegated succession of the lower, andesitic components of the BVS (Figure 24). The walk begins beneath the tuff-capped lava flows of Brown Knotts and as far as Ashness Bridge (270198) the slopes are littered with rubble from the thick beds of lavas, tuffs and breccias seen above. The explosive power of certain of the eruptions is shown by the coarse agglomerate blocks containing fragments of up to a foot across (car park at 269202). In contrast, Ashness Bridge stands upon water-freshened fine ashes whose joint systems illustrate the contraction on cooling and the later stresses imposed upon the rocks.

Beyond the bridge the frequent exposures permit the observation of dip and strike and the dip assumes its regional southeasterly trend as we pass beyond the influence of the Bleaberry Fell syncline. The generally fine tuffs are often massive but there is much evidence of the power of mechanical weathering processes to disintegrate such rocks along minor lines of weakness. The upper shoulder of the trough is reached where a footpath is signposted to Borrowdale via a footbridge

Fig 28: Watendlath Gorge

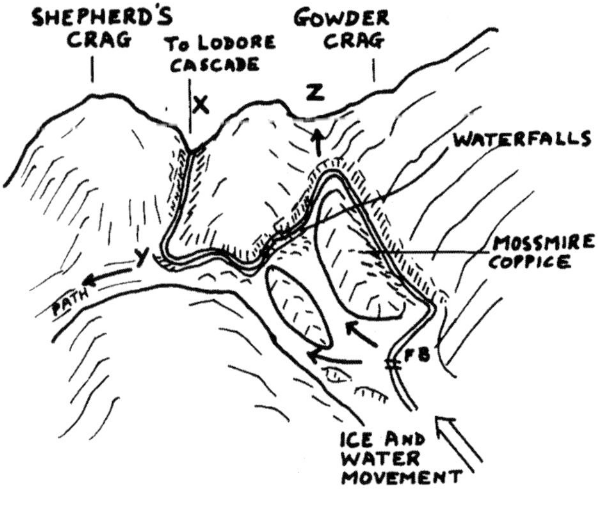

(269181) and the Watendlath valley opens out ahead.

The Borrowdale path follows Watendlath Beck downstream through its gorge section. This irregular course (Figure 28) is controlled by fault and master-joint systems trending mainly SSE-NNW and ENE-WSW, but has been further worked out by ice spilling from the upper valley by several exits (XYZ on Figure 28) and by later subglacial and marginal meltwater streams. The final selection of exit X may have been caused by an ice-mass against the shoulder at Y.

The path follows one of several ice and meltwater channels through Mossmire Coppice and then passes through the col at Y which can be seen to be ice-worked. The descent to High Lodore (262183) gives fine views of the Borrowdale alluvial flats and at the break of slope behind the buildings the Skiddaw Slate/BVS junction is crossed once more, here covered by rubble and drift although it can occasionally be seen at the beck itself. The famous Lodore Cascade is approached from the hotel (264189), the water pouring over a series of resistant lavas and tuffs.

Continuing the Watendlath transect, above the cattle grid the valley opens into a small glacial trough. The overdeepened sides are smoothed and plucked, revealing massive lava flows and tuff beds. The flat floor is built of lacustrine and alluvial deposits. During the final stages of glaciation a lakelet lay in the valley, ponded back by the rocky mass of Mossmire Coppice. The lake was drained only when the beck had cut into this rock bar to below the level of the valley floor.

The trough is terminated upvalley by a splendid rock bar on part of which sits Watendlath hamlet (Figure 29). The barrier is plastered with drift and together they impound Watendlath Tarn, itself a remnant of a more extensive upland tarn. The upper basin is well seen from the Rosthwaite footpath west of the village. Around the upper rim lie the rolling but knobbly expanses of the pre-glacial erosion surfaces stripped by ice, while the flanks are smoothed by ice and drift, this smoothing currently being destroyed by the long straight gullies cutting back through the drift and solid rock. The lower flanks and part of the basin floor are covered with hummocky drift left by ice melting in situ, while the remainder of the floor is filled with marshy alluvium and the tarn.

The rim is broken by an ice-worked col followed by the footpath to Rosthwaite (258149). As one climbs, detritus exhibits the great variety of rock type – all grades of ash, occasional breccias and many colours; green, purple, red, dun and

Fig 29: Watendlath Hamlet

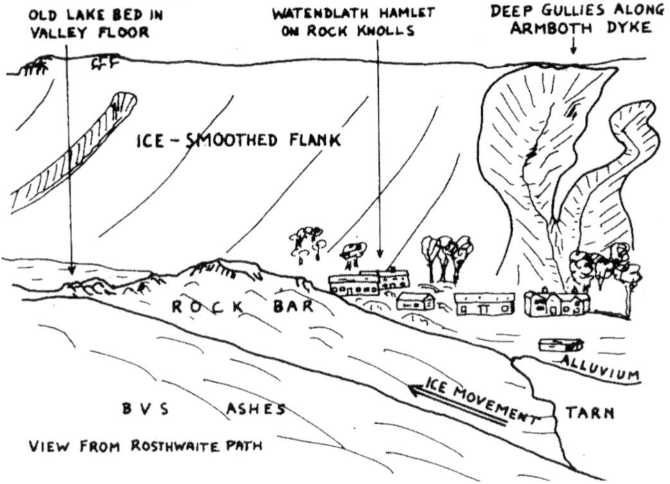

OLD LAKE BED IN VALLEY FLOOR — WATENDLATH HAMLET ON ROCK KNOLLS — DEEP GULLIES ALONG ARMBOTH DYKE

ICE - SMOOTHED FLANK

ROCK BAR

ALLUVIUM

ICE MOVEMENT

B V S ASHES TARN

VIEW FROM ROSTHWAITE PATH

frequent white patina. The most remarkable feature is the high-angle cleavage, in excess of 60° in the fine to medium andesitic ashes, which produces the shattered and slaty effect in the rocks. We are near the easternmost extension of the zone of cleaved Middle Tuffs (several hundred feet thick and extending from west of Honister Pass, across High Scawdel and Borrowdale) which produces the beautiful green and grey slates of Honister and Borrowdale. The two ravines in the east flank, Raise Gill and Greenhow gullies, are both within this cleaved zone, but their detailed courses are guided by exposures of the basic

Armboth Dike, one of the most extensive igneous dykes of the Lake District.

UPPER BORROWDALE

If only one day is available to 'do' Borrowdale, then perhaps the most economical method is to ascend King's How (258167). This can be accomplished by a relatively easy path from Watendlath, or by a path from the Red Brow car park (257158) below Frith Wood, or from Rosthwaite village itself.

Whichever is chosen, the ascent is across the thick tuffs and interbedded lavas of the Middle Tuffs, here flexed into a syncline across the Watendlath-Rosthwaite col and an anticline beneath Great Crag (Figure 24). Such a structure helps to explain the presence of the cleaved slates below King's How at Quayfoot or Rainspot Quarry (252168) rather north of the Honister-Watendlath line. On the approach to King's How from Brund Fell (265162), the dip of the beds is clearly seen as is the fault-guided marginal meltwater channel of Long Moss. First ice and then water spilled through this gap, and at one stage King's How would have been a nunatak. The smoothing effect of the ice is shown beautifully on this rocky hill, as are striations. The summit itself is built of ashes with widely spaced joints. These ashes weather to a stone colour and some of the included fragments have weathered out to give a vesicular appearance.

From the summit the views are panoramic. Directly below, the full depth of the gorge can be appreciated. Especially remarkable is the extent to which the constriction has survived the immense power of the vigorous ice-stream collected in upper Borrowdale which squeezed through this gap for more than a

Fig 30: Upper Borrowdale

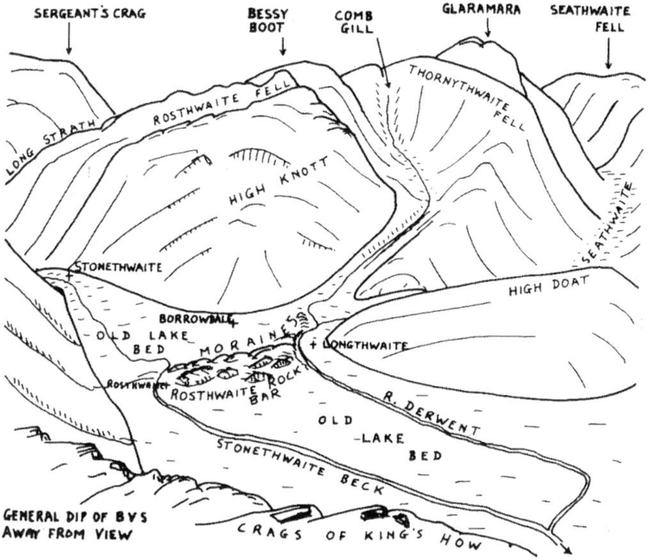

GENERAL DIP OF BVS AWAY FROM VIEW

million years. Prior to glaciation it must have been a declevity indeed! On the western flank of the gorge a small slate quarry has been opened up, but the large Quayfoot or Rainspot Quarry beside the road (252168) has long been closed. Today it is a car park and there are fine exposures showing the high-angle cleavage contrasting with the relict bedding. The spoil-heaps provide specimens of the green slate, but what are now less common are the 'rainspot' slates for which this quarry was famous. The spots are coarser fragments of dark, angular volcanic material included within the generally fine ash. Castle Crag is a magnificent 600ft knob of slate whose southern face is polished and smoothed by ice. The strong vertical jointing systems, together with the regular cleavage, have caused a slate quarry to be cut into the very summit.

North of the gorge the Hollows Skiddaw Slate-BVS junction stands out once more (Figure 26), leading to the sweep of the Skiddaw Slate fells. To the north the broad basin of Derwentwater and Bassenthwaite is laid out beyond the delta, while over all broods the mass of Skiddaw. The BVS crags of the eastern flanks show their scarp and dip structure with the knobbly, ice-torn upper surfaces. Into this wild country has been cut the Watendlath and other clefts along the joint systems.

To the south are the valleys which run down from the Great Gable-Great End mountain knot, built on BVS with the dip generally away from the observer and hence with the rocks becoming younger as one passes south (Figure 30). The two main troughs, Stonethwaite and Seathwaite, gather tributary valleys before themselves uniting at Borrowdale hamlet. It is easy to visualise snow and ice gathering in the mountains, pouring streams of ice down these valleys to pile up against the barrier of the Jaws.

Although the overall form of the landscape was sculptured during periods of heavy glaciation, eg the stripping and veneering of the upper surfaces and the gouging of corries and U-shaped troughs, many of the detailed facets of the valley scenery were produced during late stages in the glacial retreat. Ice-fronts rarely retreat steadily. Climate characteristics determine the supply of snow and ice to a glacier. As climate ameliorates the ice supply diminishes, the ice-level is lowered and the ice-front retreats; as climate deteriorates ice supply increases, the ice-level is raised and the ice-front advances. Climatic change tends to be irregular or cyclical, thus periods of ice-front stillstand alternate with periods of advance or retreat.

At a time of stillstand, débris transported by the ice piles up at the

Fig 31: Drift-plastered Roche Moutonnée at Red Brow

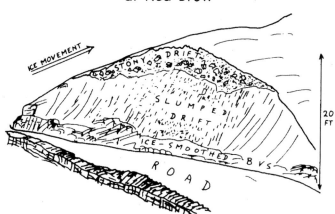

snout of the glacier thus forming a terminal moraine. With the next climatic amelioration the ice-front retreats, leaving the moraine lying across the valley. Such moraines may well abut against a rock bar which held up the glacier snout. Whether in combination or separately, such obstructions were capable of impeding meltwaters from the shrunken glaciers, and frequently lakes built up behind the rock bars and moraines until the water level reached the lowest point of overflow. This ablation stream then proceeded to cut into the barrier, and as the exit level was lowered so was the lake level.

Such a sequence of terminal moraines is exhibited in several Lake District valleys, most clearly in the Coniston valley at Nibthwaite and in upper Borrowdale at Rosthwaite. In this latter example a series of sequential glacial lakes were penned behind barriers (1, 2, 3, 4 on Figure 23). The first, Lake Rosthwaite, was impounded by the Jaws constriction at Red Brow (255159). The extreme flatness of this old lake bed, up to half a mile wide, is evident from Red Brow and is still floodable. Also at Red Brow, approximately 100 yards below the car park, is a roche moutonnée truncated by the road cut and plastered with stony drift (Figure 31). The red earthy matrix encloses grey-green BVS fragments, subangular and up to 1 foot long. This may be a remnant of

Fig 32: Rosthwaite Relationships

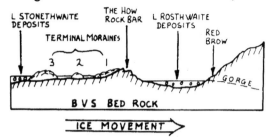

L STONETHWAITE DEPOSITS — THE HOW ROCK BAR — L ROSTHWAITE DEPOSITS — RED BROW

TERMINAL MORAINES

3 2 1

GORGE

B V S BED ROCK

ICE MOVEMENT →

a terminal moraine piled up against the rock barrier.

Rosthwaite village, the location for Walpole's 'Herries' novels, sits upon a magnificent valley obstruction which is a combination of rock bar and terminal moraine (Figure 32). The rock bar, known as The How (257147), is a group of roche moutonnées up to 30ft high of blue medium tuffs. Their upvalley flanks are smoothed while the downvalley sides are rugged from the plucking action of the ice, the summit being several whaleback ridges pointing in the direction of ice movement.

Piled against the back of The How is the front of three moraines (1 on Figure 32), each representing a stillstand in the ice-front. The second is a small moraine roll (2 on Figure 32) in the fields some 30 yards upvalley, while upstream again the principal Stonethwaite moraine (3 on Figure 32) is a collection of lobate masses up to

30ft high. It is impinged upon near its east and west ends by Stonethwaite Beck and the River Derwent respectively. Behind this moraine, Lake Stonethwaite was impounded, extending to the junction of Greenup Gill and Langstrath Beck (2 on Figure 23). Two post-glacial river terraces cut into these lake-bed deposits mark stages in the lowering of the exit through the Rosthwaite rock bar and moraine complex. The Stonethwaite Beck is still forced to wriggle tightly before squeezing through where the road now passes (259146).

The character of the moraine is best seen at its western end where the Derwent has undercut its outer edge. Walk from the village westwards along a farm track to the ford (254148). Turn south up the Derwent along the artificial levee built to prevent flooding of the old lake bed. The asymmetrical roche moutonnée of the rock bar stands out before the lobate grassy moraine is reached. A huge angular block some 20ft long is perched on the side of the moraine in front of Longthwaite. At this farm the stream is actively undercutting the moraine front, laying bare the stony unsorted material in its red matrix. A small river terrace has been cut below the western face of the moraine and the stream is some 25ft below the old lake flat east of the moraine. West of the Rosthwaite moraine another flat occurs as far as a smaller moraine south of Burthwaite Bridge (255139). Here a small body of water, Lake Borrowdale, may have lain (3 on Figure 23), perhaps connected to the final lake in the Seathwaite valley (4 on Figure 23).

The entrance to this last valley is guarded by a well-defined moraine extending much of the way across the valley, and capped by Thornythwaite Farm (256134). As one turns into the valley at Seatoller Bridge (246138) it is worth glancing westwards over Seatoller hamlet to the fine hanging valley of Little Gatesgarthdale Hause Gill up which the Honister

Fig 33: The Seathwaite Glacial Trough

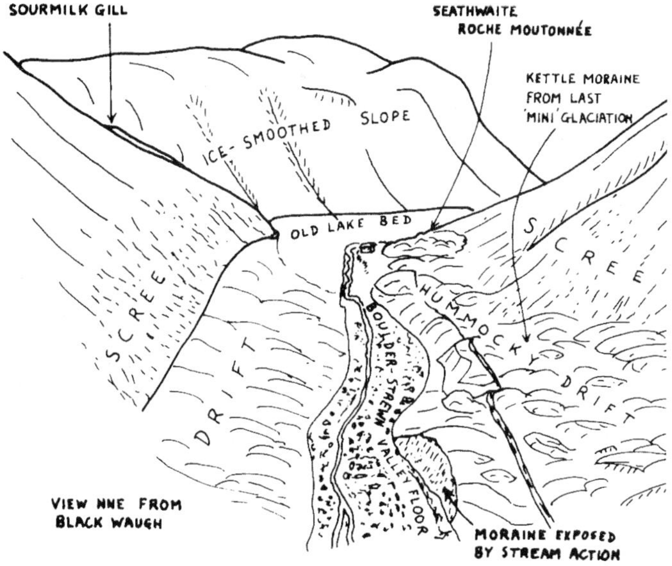

SOURMILK GILL

SEATHWAITE ROCHE MOUTONNÉE

KETTLE MORAINE FROM LAST 'MINI' GLACIATION

ICE-SMOOTHED SLOPE

OLD LAKE BED

SCREE

SCREE

HUMMOCKY

DRIFT

DRIFT

BOULDER-STREWN VALLEY FLOOR

VIEW NNE FROM BLACK WAUGH

MORAINE EXPOSED BY STREAM ACTION

Pass road climbs. Beyond the Thornythwaite moraine the old lake bed of Seathwaite valley is very flat while ahead the sweep of the flanks show classic over-deepening and hanging valleys.

Near the upper limit of the lake bed, Seathwaite hamlet sits at the foot of another moraine-plastered rock bar, and as one rounds this ridge an amazing change takes place. Until this point the valley floor has been flat and well cultivated but now it becomes wild and truly an upland valley. The walk upvalley from the farmsteads is across a boulder-strewn wilderness, the boulders being not only in the broad stream bed, but also littered in the debris which clutters the whole valley floor. A convenient location from which to appreciate the features is the buttress of Black Waugh below Aaron Crags (230104, Figure 33). The classic U-shape of the glaciated trough sweeps down to Borrowdale with the shoulder of overdeepening and the smoothed valley sides. Into the western flank have been cut two deep notches, the ravines through which Sourmilk Gill emerges from the hanging valley and corrie hollow of Gillercomb, and Styhead Gill cascades down Taylorgill Force (230109). The eastern flank is being shattered by gullies, stone chutes and screes.

In the valley floor the lake bed extends away beyond the Seathwaite ridge, above which the lower flanks and floor are covered with hummocky drift. This, like that seen along the road below Honister Pass, is very fresh in form and belongs to the last mini-glaciation of some 8,800 years ago when a colder climatic spell lasting some 500 years permitted sufficient snow accumulation for ice-tongues to push out of the deeper more-sheltered corries. This last Seathwaite glacier pushed as far as the hamlet and then much of the ice became stagnant, melted in situ, and deposited this hummocky drift. Below Stockley Bridge one large mound is being actively undercut by the stream which provides continuously fresh faces. It is a dark-grey stony drift, with larger blocks up to 3ft long and completely unsorted. Such readily available debris, plus the thick drift cover being dissected in the upper sections of Grainsgill, the plentiful mounds of boulder moraine across the Styhead Gill hanging-valley lip, and the numerous active stone chutes, together provide enormous quantities of load for the stream. Much of this material is moved only at times of heavy rain or snow melt, but in such times the swirling roaring torrent is very impressive.

Stockley Bridge stands upon a rock step which marks the trough end of the Seathwaite valley. The toughened largely andesitic fine ashes have an irregular jointing system, and the cleft through which the beck flows has been worked along a series of close-set vertical joints. The step in the valley floor at this point is the result of the Grainsgill and Styhead ice-streams meeting, thereby increasing their erosive power and resulting in further deepening from this point downvalley.

The climb from Stockley Bridge to Taylorgill Force is up the local strike and across a series of ash beds from fine to extremely coarse. These are the upper sections of the Grey Knotts or Lower Andesite Group near the stream, succeeded upwards by increasingly acid materials belonging to the Airy's Bridge Group of dacites, rhyolites, felsites and their tuffs. A typical felsitic ash of this series, found especially on the flanks of Base Brown (225115), is blue when fresh, weathers to a whitish patina and has an overall columnar structure. It contains approximately 70 per cent silica and 20 per cent alumina. Aaron Crags is built of the alternating andesitic and acid tuffs of the Seathwaite Fell Tuff group. The increasing dominance of more acidic beds among the higher series of the BVS succession is typical of volcanic episodes. The normal sequence is for a basic opening spell, followed by intermediate andesitic series, and finally, materials with a high silica content such as rhyolites or

Fig 34: BVS Succession From Stonethwaite to Glaramara (after Oliver)

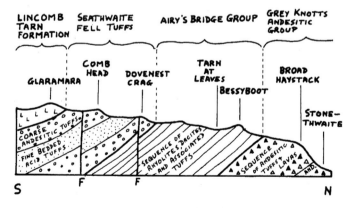

57

felsites and their tuffs. A similar multiple sandwich of basic and acid materials is seen along the well-known track from Coniston, up Church Beck and on to Coniston Old Man.

While at Seathwaite a climb up Sourmilk Gill is worthwhile, again over a series of tuffs and occasional very coarse agglomerates. The stream cuts through the lip of the hanging valley across an excellent example of a coarse andesitic tuff – grey-green in colour with many darker fragments in the fine-grained matrix, indicating a violent explosive eruption producing pyroclastic materials. This lip contains much drift but this is less impressive than the prodigious heaps dumped in the mouth of Styhead. Gillercomb is an amphitheatre frowned upon by crags. Although now lacking a tarn, the floor is still very boggy. The northeast orientation of this corrie hollow accords with the most common direction for Lake District corries-the aspect which affords maximum shade for snow and ice.

A final scramble from Seathwaite will take in the disused plumbago mine (232127), a unique deposit in the Lake District and the origin of the local pencil industry. Plumbago or graphite is an amorphous, ie non-crystalline, form of carbon believed to have been injected into the BVS as a condensation product of some deep-seated intrusion, possibly the Eskdale Granite. The source of carbon may be the underlying Skiddaw Slates which, as water-lain sedimentaries, included fossils containing carbon. The theory is that during the intrusions of the Devonian period, emanating heat vaporised some of this carbon which then passed upwards to condense within the structure of the country rocks, in this case diorite. The spoil-heaps may yield specimens of the soft black graphite within the dark igneous material.

Fig 35: Texture Grading of Lava Flow Rosthwaite Fell

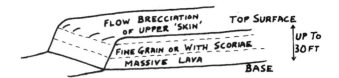

The mine, worked from the seventeenth until the late nineteenth century, operated along several levels between 500 and 1,000ft OD, cut into the central diorite dike and its surrounding blue diabase. The levels were connected by vertical shafts and one such shaft is still open, giving access to those correctly equipped to descend 75ft or so to Old Man's Level.

The fells to the east and west of the Seathwaite valley, climbing to Glaramara (248108) and Great Gable (211103) respectively, are built upon similar series of the BVS dipping generally southwards. Either is worth a full-day scramble which is, by any route, strenuous. A general guide to the geological succession is given by Figure 34, which takes the Glaramara transect from Stonethwaite hamlet (263138). Perhaps the most impressive components of such a transect are the range of rock type associated with volcanic outbursts and the immense amounts of material produced by them, for the route passes onwards and upwards over successively younger formations, totalling several thousand feet in thickness.

One specific feature may be noted, that of flow-brecciation in lava flows, which is well illustrated in the flows of the Grey Knotts Andesitic Group, eg on the approach to Bessyboot (258125). Examination shows the surfaces of some of these flows to be brecciated and similar in appearance to an agglomerate. As lava is extruded its outer sections are cooled rapidly, forming a skin of solid material, while the inner portions remain viscous. Should movement continue, the outer skin will be broken and crumpled to a clinker-like form. Eventually the whole mass cools and solidifies, leaving the inner portions typically fine-grained while the originally solidified outer fragments are now cemented into a similar fine-grained matrix, closely resembling a true pyroclastic breccia (Figure 35). A general guide to identification is that on the weathered surface of the flow breccias it is the fragmental material which is usually recessed, ie less resistant, whereas in true breccias it is the fragments which stand out, ie more resistant.

Chapter 4

The Ullswater District

ULLSWATER LIES athwart exposures of both the BVS and the Skiddaw Slates (Figure 36). The contrasting scenery produced by them is well seen both on the local scale around the lake itself and on the regional scale where, from a number of vantage points above the lake, panoramic views of the BVS of the Helvellyn range can be compared with the Skiddaw Slate topography of the Skiddaw range. In addition there is the very distinctive country of Great and Little Mell Fen developed on the famous Mell Fell Conglomerate.

The lake is the second largest in the Lake District. If its inverse S-shape is straightened it stretches for almost eight miles from Pooley Bridge to Patterdale, where its former length has been reduced by the post-glacial alluvium of Grisedale and Goldrill Becks. In places the lake exceeds 200ft in depth, and the whole trough exhibits many of the features typical of glaciation.

From Penrith, where there is an M6 junction, the A592 gives easy access at Pooley Bridge, while from the south-west the road descends from the Kirkstone Pass. The locality also lies on one of the best-known walking traverses of the eastern Lake District, from Haweswater

and High Street, to Patterdale across Helvellyn to Keswick. It is possible to examine the principal rock types and to appreciate the principal landscape elements without leaving a surfaced road, although as with all of the Lake District, it is by walking the country that a deeper understanding comes.

A trip along either shore of the lake quickly reveals how well the major landscape types are correlated with the three rock groups. The low, smooth improved farmland along much of the lakeside has been developed on Skiddaw Slates, the craggy country above is of BVS and the series of smooth dome-like hills to the north and north-east are of Mell Fell Conglomerate sitting upon the Borrowdale Volcanic materials.

The presence of this 'window' of Lower Ordovician Skiddaw Slate within the younger BVS is explained by the local structure (Figure 37). Ullswater lies along an asymmetrical anticline with the steep limb to the south, which has been pierced along its crest. Through millions of years, the erosional agencies have produced an inverted landscape (Figure 38).

In detail, the structure is more complex. The anticline has been riven and broken by three systems

Fig 36: Solid Geology of the Ullswater Area

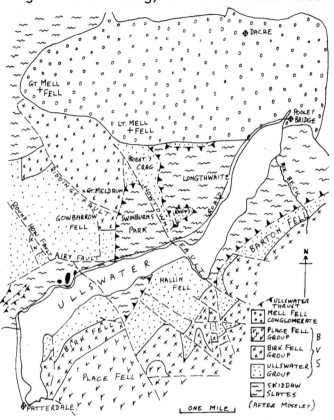

Legend:

- ▲ ULLSWATER THRUST
- ○ MELL FELL CONGLOMERATE
- ∨ PLACE FELL GROUP ⎫
- × BIRK FELL GROUP ⎬ B V S
- ∴ ULLSWATER GROUP ⎭
- ⌐ SKIDDAW SLATES

(AFTER MOSELEY)

ONE MILE

of faults: a group of low-angle faults, known as the Ullswater Thrust whereby the Skiddaw Slates have squeezed up the BVS above them; two series of high-angle faults with predominantly northerly and north-westerly trends which have produced lateral and vertical movement. The block diagrams (Figure 38) illustrate such faults.

In consequence, the alignment of the Ullswater anticline is broken into segments by lateral movements along the Scalehow and Howtown

61

Fig 37: Structural Lines of Ullswater

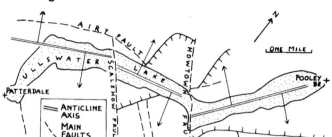

faults, the two most important NW-trending faults. The kink in the lake caused by the wrenching along the Howtown Fault has enhanced the scenic beauty by bringing in a succession of vistas along the lower and upper lake sections. From the top of Hallin Fell (433198) the alignment of this fault can be followed to the north of the lake by the abrupt front from Birk Crag to Priest's Crag (Figure

39). This front indicates that the fault has moved vertically as well as laterally.

The basin of Skiddaw Slates across Swinburn's Park emerges from beneath the BVS of Gowbarrow Fell (407218) and Great Meldrum (415223), and is brought to an abrupt end against the Howtown Fault at Birk Crag. To the east the triangular Longthwaite lowland repeats

Fig 38: The Essentials of Ullswater's Structure

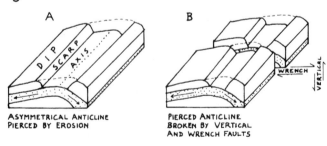

ASYMMETRICAL ANTICLINE
PIERCED BY EROSION

PIERCED ANTICLINE
BROKEN BY VERTICAL
AND WRENCH FAULTS

Fig 39: Scenery North of Ullswater

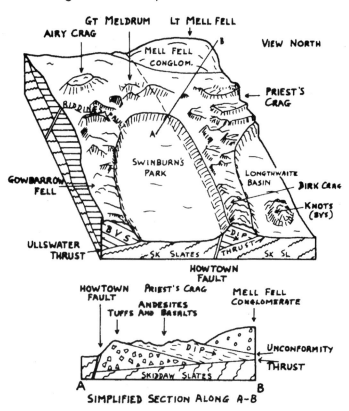

the Skiddaw Slate topography, but this time the slates disappear northwards beneath the Devonian Mell Fell Conglomerate. The Ullswater Thrust, upon which the BVS and Devonian rocks sit (Figure 40), is in reality a system of low-angle faults correctly known as an 'imbricate' system.

On either side of Hallin Fell to the south of the lake are similar low-lying areas developed on the Slates, the small Sandwick triangle to the west, faulted

Fig 40: Simplified Cross-Section North of Ullswater to Illustrate the Thrust/BVS Relationship

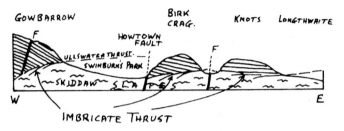

The BVS sit upon the thrust eg Gowbarrow, Birk Crag, Knots

against the Scalehow Fault, and the long area below the crags of Barton Fell to the north-east (Figure 41).

In all the localities, north and south of Ullswater, there are few good exposures of the Skiddaw Slates, for this lower land is extensively masked by glacial drift, usually boulder clay.

It is on such lower softer areas that the large nineteenth-century houses with their landscaped gardens and parks were laid out, and which today provide much of the varied mature woodland of the lakeshores, eg the estate of Gowbarrow (4321), although sufficient open country remains to recall the medieval deer parks

Fig 41: Scarp and Dip Scenery Across Barton Fell

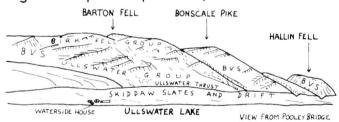

of Gowbarrow and Glencoyne. Exposures are most likely close by the junction with the overlying BVS, eg below Gate Crags (424222), Glencoyne Park (383195) and particularly in Aik Beck (473227) south of the lake. Wherever they are exposed they show a similar range of characteristics. The rock types vary from true slates, through shales and mudstones to tuffs, and are always dark grey to black in colour. Fossils are rare - a few graptolites - while water-lain igneous tuffs become increasingly frequent in the uppermost beds, indicating the onset of the volcanic episode. The rocks vary from soft sandy shales in Aik Beck to hard brittle mudstones in Glencoyne Park, but the low-lying scenery suggests their general ease of weathering. Cleavage and jointing vary, but the structure is very complex with intense folding and contortion.

Hallin Fell may also be used as a viewpoint for working through the BVS succession. Around Ullswater, approximately 8,500ft of the lower BVS are exposed and have been divided by Moseley into four groups (Table 2).

The sequence locally is typical of the BVS generally: a lower succession of basic rocks, eg basalts, andesites followed by the increasing occurrence of acidic

Table 2: Geological Succession of the Ullswater District

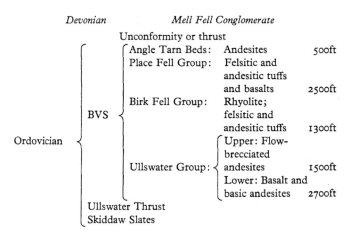

Devonian			Mell Fell Conglomerate	
		Unconformity or thrust		
		Angle Tarn Beds:	Andesites	500ft
		Place Fell Group:	Felsitic and andesitic tuffs and basalts	2500ft
	BVS	Birk Fell Group:	Rhyolite; felsitic and andesitic tuffs	1300ft
Ordovician		Ullswater Group:	Upper: Flow-brecciated andesites	1500ft
			Lower: Basalt and basic andesites	2700ft
		Ullswater Thrust		
		Skiddaw Slates		

types, eg felsites and rhyolites. As above Haweswater, there is clear evidence that many of the beds are of submarine deposition, eg bedded tuffs showing grading, typical of settling in water. The locality has a full range of types from fine-grained black basalts on the slopes of Hallin Fell to coarse felsitic tuffs on the eastern flanks of Place Fell at Black Crag (415175). The coloration is generally dark and the topography developed on these volcanic materials is distinctively craggy. There are many fine exposures, and frequently individual beds can be followed for some distance which makes for splendid field-mapping conditions, eg along Barton Fell (Figure 41).

Of course, the structure is complicated by the faulting systems, and this makes correlation between the different topographic blocks difficult. When aided by weathering processes, however, the faulting has the benefit of working out individual hill masses. These separate blocks have variable dip and strike characteristics, but in general the northern limb of the anticline is the shallower, with dips from 10° to 45°, trending from NW to NNE. The steeper southern limb dips from 30° to 60° in a general SE direction.

The Birk Crag–Priest's Crag ridge (Figure 39) exposes the lowest BVS beds found locally in the Lower Ullswater Group. The scarp faces the Howtown Fault and the abrupt south-west-facing crags are of dark, coarse andesitic tuffs, very similar, in fact, to those found near the summit of Hallin Fell. There are approximately 1,500ft of these tuffs, and a traverse from the Howtown Fault at Gate Crags (424222) NNE to the foot of Little Mell Fell crosses this sequence. This is followed on Priest's Crag itself by 200ft of andesites which grow increasingly basic, becoming basalts, totalling 800ft, and finally returning to 300ft of andesites before disappearing beneath the Mell Fell Conglomerate (425235). The well-defined perimeter, the simple dip structure and the distinctive weathering of the individual beds make this a particularly good locality for field mapping and specimen collection, and it is easily accessible from a road.

The craggy hills from Gowbarrow Fell to Glencoynedale are developed on the materials of the Upper Ullswater Group, mostly andesites with occasional basalt flows and occasional coarse tuffs, eg between Airy Crag and the Riddings Fault (409222).

Jointing is usually well developed, rectangular and tangential to the dip which results in a rubble of large blocks (eg Airy Crag at Gowbarrow Fell summit (407219) except near fault lines where shattering is more common.

The youngest BVS rocks found north of the lake are the Birk Fell beds of the Great Meldrum locality (415224). Unfortunately, drift covers much of the outcrop although exposures can be examined on the east flank of Gowbarrow Fell (412218) near the National Trust boundary wall, showing the range of pale rhyolites and rhyolitic tuffs typical of this group.

South of the lake the faulting is more complex and subdivides the area around Hallin Fell into separate blocks mostly of the Ullswater and Birk Fell materials. Hallin Fell itself contains the most complete sequence of the Ullswater Group and is dominated by andesites and basalts with a whole sequence of rock types from pale grey through dark blue, purple to brick red and with textures from fine to coarse with speckling common and occasional vesicles.

The three valleys of Fusedale, Bannerdale and Boredale are fault-guided, the former pair illustrating the effects of the locally important NS fault direction, and the hill masses such as Steel Knotts and Sleet Fell are fault-defined. From a viewpoint north of the lake on Gate Crag, Hallin Fell stands out as the dominant hill mass. This fell is a fault-defined mass of beds tilted steeply to the south-west with separate beds well defined. The basalts are usually more massive with widely spaced joints. In colour both basalts and andesites are dark green to dark blue-grey, the basalts in particular having small phenocrysts of felspar and there are white calcite patches in the generally fine-grained matrix. The andesites may have a perlitic texture and deep-red clusters of garnet, but their most distinctive characteristic is the flow-brecciation at the top and base of flows (Figure 35).

Tuffs are found most frequently near the base of the Fell, up to coarse in texture, generally dark to purplish in colour and seen in knobby crags.

Near the summit of Hallin Fell, outcrops of a bright-red rock occur at the top of a lava flow. This is ferruginous staining and may be due to the contemporaneous weathering when the flow was originally exposed, or to oxidation as the result of solutions percolating from a former covering of red Permo-Triassic rocks, since removed. Such ease of percolation suggests, too, the proximity of a fault zone.

A S-N transect from St Peter's Church (435191) to Kailpot Crag across Hallin Fell yields a typical sequence of the Lower Ullswater Group in a very short distance.

Barton Fell (Figure 41) exhibits a fine series of crags of the basalts and andesites separated by more

Fig 42: Glacial Trough of Bannerdale Cut Into Lavas and Tuffs

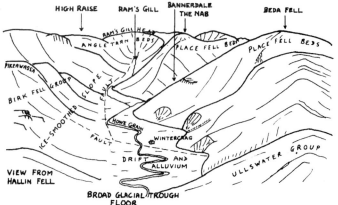

easily eroded tuffs which form the benches on which grass and scree accumulates. Upwards, the more rhyolitic Birk Fell Group comes in. A transect up Aik Beck from the road (468235) to Brown Rigg gives a sequence across the Skiddaw Slates and the BVS. From Brown Rigg the flat open top of Askham Fell, with its numerous remains of ancient occupance, eg tumuli and a Roman road, can be seen to the north-east.

Southwards from Hallin Fell the smooth, symmetrical glaciated valleys of Fusedale, Bannerdale (Figure 42) and Boredale, whence flowed feeder tongues of ice into the main Ullswater glacier, bite deeply into the hill masses until the corrie-heads at Ramsgill Head (440129) and Buck Crag (421142). Above these crags lie the remnants of the rolling upper erosion surface of the High Street range, in excess of 2,400ft.

Each of the valleys provides beautiful walks more sheltered than the open fells, but the glacial smoothing and post-glacial deposition have left few exposures and little evidence of the faults which guide the valleys. Screes - some still in motion - and drift are plentiful, while near the corrie-hollows or trough-heads the typical hummocky drift of the final ice-retreat stages are found, eg above Dalehead Farm in Boredale (4316). The fault-defined and glacially bevelled hill masses of Pikeawassa and Beda Fell are developed on the succession of lavas and tuffs from the Upper Ullswater Group through the Place Fell sequence, with tuffs generally dominant over lavas, although the principal crags indicate the presence of the resistant flows.

To the south-west, the higher BVS of Place Fell are mainly a wide range of felsitic tuffs and bedded tuffs – Place Fell summit itself being a broken mass of coarse and medium tuffs. Once again the principal crags from the Knight to High Dod follow a thick group of basalt and andesite lava flows. This mass west of the Scalehow Fault is broken by a number of faults, master joints, and veins trending generally NW or N. These can often be traced as furrows or gullies, perhaps hidden by screes, and with frequent white-quartz rubble; eg seen from the road at Glencoyne Park north of Ullswater, a series of gullies runs down the face of Birk Fell. The range from basic to acid materials is again indicated by the generally paler colours of the silica-rich acid materials. Cleavage is usually poor, but there is a zone where pressures have caused a coarse cleavage. A series of small disused quarries stretching from below the lava crags from Patterdale to High Dod reveal this zone of greenish fine-grained tuffs.

THE MELL FELL CONGLOMERATE

This mass, some six miles EW and two miles NS, overlies the Ordovician materials and produces the distinctive series of dome-like hills from Dun Mallard at Pooley Bridge (467245), across Soulby Fell and Little Mell Fell to Great Mell Fell (Figure 43).

Although called a conglomerate, much of its material is sub-angular and clearly has not travelled far from its place of origin. The rock has a coarse, pink to brown matrix within which fragments from gravels to blocks 3ft across are set in a very rough form of bedding.

Fig 43: Northern Flanks of Great and Little Mell Fell

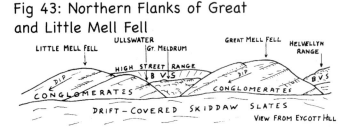

The predominant material is Silurian Coniston Grit similar to that found in the southern Lake District. The local origin of the material, in a locality where no such rocks exist in the solid today, has been explained by the removal of an earlier cover. It has been postulated that in Devonian times, when this region was a landmass, continental erosion was taking place and hill or mountain masses to the north and west were composed of the Silurian grits. The weathered material formed large detrital cones and fans at the foot of the hill masses which were consolidated and remain in part today as the Mell Fell Conglomerate, even though their solid parents have disappeared completely. These conglomerates overlie the Ordovician Skiddaw Slates and BVS unconformably and relate to the patches of Polygenetic Conglomerate found in the Cross Fell inlier at the foot of the Pennines ten miles to the east.

The smoothing and doming have reduced exposures, but the most accessible is at Pooley Bridge where the lakeside road has cut into the southern flank of Dun Mallard Hill (467243). Here sections up to 10ft thick expose the irregular bedding. Lenses of gravel separate coarser beds with subangular blocks of grey Coniston Grits, and occasional darker blocks of volcanic materials set in the pinkish matrix give a very good impression of the detrital cone origin. There is some purplish staining very typical of the conglomerates formed in the Cross Fell Inlier.

For the walker, Airy Crag on Gowbarrow Fell (408219) gives perhaps the best overall impression of the full sweep of the conglomerate hills, while on the north Eycott Hill (388296) has an open view across the Troutbeck valley. It is from the northern side that the shallow easterly dip is best seen, from the scarp steps appearing on the north-western face of Great Mell Fell. The minor road westwards from Dacre (459265) follows the length of the partially drift-covered outcrop, and occasional exposures may be seen in the streams, eg in Dacre Beck and Dacre Bridge (452260).

Although the entire district was submerged by ice, the most spectacular scenic effects were achieved by a less-complete glaciation. A major valley-glacier moved down the Ullswater valley, fed by corries and side valleys such as the Red Tarn corrie, Grisedale, Boredale and Fusedale. These provided a supply which meant an ice thickness of up to 900ft with considerable erosive capacity, giving the rock steps in the basin shown by the irregular floor of the lake and the ice smoothing and plucking so evident on the flanks. Above the ice margins, marginal meltwater channels were cut, paralleling the ice-front being seen today, particularly along the northern side of the valley, as in the series from Priest's Crag past Watermillock Church. They are identifiable by their broad floor, which is often marshy, and by the absence of a significant stream.

ADDITIONAL FOOT TRANSECT IN THE GLENCOYNEDALE AREA

From the road junction at Glencoyne Park (399199), walk up the Aira Beck. Near the junction the stream cuts into dark volcanic material which seems to be the neck of a volcanic vent in the Skiddaw Slates through which once poured the BVS material. At about 300yd upstream the gentle Skiddaw Slates give away to the craggy BVS on Airy Crag at Aira Force and the stream runs through the Upper Ullswater tuffs and lavas. At Dockray the stream flows in from the west while a much wider valley opens out northwards. This is a splendid ice spillway which curves round from Ulcat Row and has the characteristic wide flat bottom with minute stream. This once supplied ice to the main Ullswater glacier.

Follow the path running southwards by the Birk Fell knoll of Round Howe via the drift-masked areas of Watermillock Common and Brown Hills across the Airy Fault at Swinside Knot (379197) to Glencoynedale. The path runs along the very steep valley, which is the core of the Ullswater anticline. Walk down the stream where andesites and basalts can be seen, until at 378185 the Ullswater Thrust brings in some good exposures of Skiddaw Slate. The walk along the road to the starting point produces cuttings into the glacial drift and solifluction materials.

While in the upper Ullswater valley it is worth the one and a half mile walk up the Glenridding valley to the Greenside Mine (365175). This was the largest lead mine in the Lake District and is the best preserved, having closed only in 1959. Although worked in the eighteenth century when the lead ore was sent by packhorse to Keswick for smelting, it was only after 1825 that the mine developed fully and its own smelter installed. Output averaged 1,000 tons per year and the profitability was reflected in the relatively intensive capitalisation of the plant. For example, there was a power generation system which drew waters from Red Tarn and Keppelcove Tarn through a one and a quarter mile open watercourse, and this was replaced during the 1890s by some of the first electrical equipment seen in the Lake District.

The workings were a series of levels between 1,800ft and 2,500ft OD into a spur of the Helvellyn mass. The galena occurs as stringers in quartz veins and is found along with barytes, zinc blende and silver. The principal veins are set within BVS felspathic ashes and lavas, strike 20° east of north and dip to the east, approximately 18° from the vertical. Various buildings including washing and dressing plants and rows of miners' cottages survive to tell of this famous and prosperous mine. Extensive spoil heaps still yield crystals despite the depredations of the many visitors.

Chapter 5

Langdale

THIS CHAPTER covers Great Langdale valley and its neighbouring fells. Much of the nature of the country can be viewed from the valley roads and paths, but transects on to the uplands are outlined and involve some stiff walks and scrambles, although I must admit that I have not done any mapping or sketching while hanging from Glimmer Crag!

Great Langdale is, in Lake District terms, the 'big country'. Here in the heart of the Borrowdale Volcanic outcrop, structural and weathering processes have combined to produce some of the deepest valleys, the steepest slopes and crags so beloved of climbers, and some of the highest country,

including access to Scafell, which, at 3,210ft is the highest summit in England.

It is wild craggy country (Figure 44) apparently without pattern or order, and like so much of the Lake District it needs to be approached via stages of complexity. Reduced to its structural essentials, Great Langdale is aligned along the axis of an anticline running WSW-ENE (Figure 45), while a parallel syncline runs to the north, from Scafell (215072), across Esk Hause to High White Stones (280095). Another syncline runs approximately along Greenburn to the south, while to the south of this again the Coniston Range BVS succession dips away to the SE. Thus the 10,000ft or more

Fig 44: BVS Scenery of the Langdale Pikes

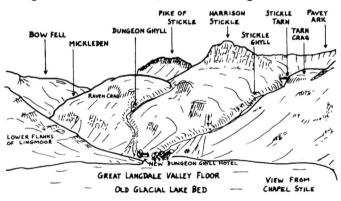

BOW FELL
MICKLEDEN
DUNGEON GHYLL
PIKE OF STICKLE
HARRISON STICKLE
STICKLE TARN
PAVEY ARK
STICKLE GHYLL
TARN CRAG
RAVEN CRAG
LOWER FLANKS OF LINGMOOR
NEW DUNGEON GHYLL HOTEL
GREAT LANGDALE VALLEY FLOOR
OLD GLACIAL LAKE BED
VIEW FROM CHAPEL STILE

Fig 45: Main Structural Lines of the Langdale District

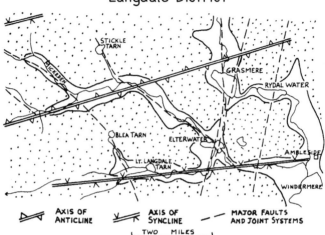

STICKLE TARN
MICKLEDEN
GRASMERE
RYDAL WATER
BLEA TARN
ELTERWATER
LT. LANGDALE TARN
AMBLESIDE
WINDERMERE
AXIS OF ANTICLINE
AXIS OF SYNCLINE
MAJOR FAULTS AND JOINT SYSTEMS
TWO MILES

of the Ordovician Borrowdale Volcanic materials have been flexed by Devonian folding and the whole structure is a double anticline with some overfolding (Figure 46).

Through time, the arch of the anticline was pierced in similar fashion to that of Ullswater (Chapter 4). The well-jointed rocks of the anticline were then attacked

Fig 46: The Langdale Anticlinorium

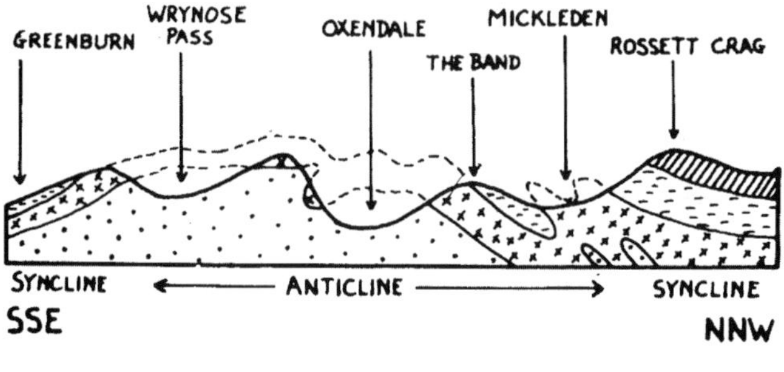

GREENBURN
WRYNOSE PASS
OXENDALE
THE BAND
MICKLEDEN
ROSSETT CRAG
SYNCLINE
ANTICLINE
SYNCLINE
SSE
NNW

Fig 47: Generalised Geology of part of Great Langdale

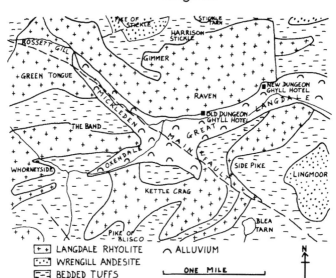

PIKE OF STICKLE · STICKLE TARN · HARRISON STICKLE · ROSSETT GILL · GIMMER · GREEN TONGUE · MICKLEDEN · RAVEN · NEW DUNGEON GHYLL HOTEL · LANGDALE · THE BAND · OLD DUNGEON GHYLL HOTEL · GREAT · MAIN FAULT · WHORNEYSIDE · OXENDALE · SIDE PIKE · LINGMOOR · KETTLE CRAG · PIKE OF BLISCO · BLEA TARN

+ + LANGDALE RHYOLITE
⋯ WRENGILL ANDESITE
▭ BEDDED TUFFS
∩ ALLUVIUM

ONE MILE

N

until a deep cleft was formed, and within the Ice Age of the past two million years its form modified to the classic U-shape. Today, Great Langdale is flanked by steep scarp slopes, from which beds dip away to north and south. We would expect, therefore, that the oldest rocks would be exposed on the valley floor and the youngest rocks on the upper surface of the dip slopes. This assumption is only partly accurate, for the geological map (Figure 47) shows that younger beds appear successively towards the ENE. So

we must add a further complication to the anticline – it pitches to the ENE and such a structure indeed brings in successively younger beds in that direction (Figure 48).

The local geologic succession (Table 3) is dominated by various tuffs, that is, ashes and other pyroclastic materials deposited both on land and beneath the ocean, while lavas become more frequent higher in the succession. In addition there is the complication, and apparent anomaly, of an intrusive material called 'rhyolite'. By all

Fig 48: Great Langdale - Strike and Dip in BVS

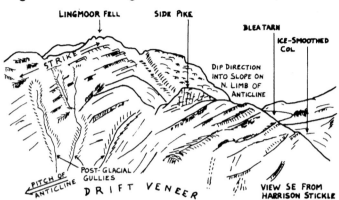

LINGMOOR FELL   SIDE PIKE

BLEA TARN

ICE-SMOOTHED COL

STRIKE

DIP DIRECTION INTO SLOPE ON N. LIMB OF ANTICLINE

POST-GLACIAL GULLIES

PITCH OF ANTICLINE

DRIFT VENEER

VIEW SE FROM HARRISON STICKLE

normal classifications rhyolite is an acid-extrusive lava, but locally it is the standard term given to fairly fine-grained, pink to brown rocks which were intruded into the Bedded Tuffs soon after their deposition and which have many of the characteristics of thick lavas.

These rhyolites form much of the floor and slopes of Great Langdale, including the famous climbing crags below the Pikes - Glimmer, Thorn and Raven. In the valley floor their few exposures indicate a close jointing system, which helps to account for their removal, but on the slopes they are frequently massive and form the resistant crags. Such jointing as they possess is near-vertical and helps to form the cracks which, allied to the compact nature of the rock, make them so marvellous for climbing.

Faults cross the area in predominantly SE-NW directions,

Table 3: BVS in Great Langdale

Intrusive Rhyolites	Up to 800ft
Upper Rhyolites	
Felsitic and Basic Tuffs	250ft
Wrengill Andesites	Up to 500ft
Bedded Tuffs	2500ft
Mosedale Andesites	1300ft

although few have massive displacements, eg the largest known is 900ft along Yeastyrigg Gill. Many are better thought of as masterjoint systems and certainly they may be divided into two groups – dip joints or strike joints (Figure 49). The strike-joint systems have helped in the working out of the main alignment of Great Langdale and Oxendale, while the major dip-fault is the line from west of Lingmoor along Mickleden, up Rossett Gill, over Esk Hause and eventually through Aaron Slack east of Great Gable. Further joints guide the alignment of the large straight gullies in the north side of

Fig 49: Strike and Dip Faults

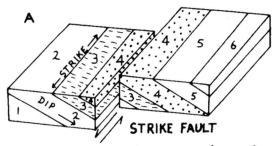

STRIKE FAULT

DISPLACEMENTS SHOWN ARE LATERAL (WRENCH)
VERTICAL MOVEMENTS ARE EQUALLY LIKELY

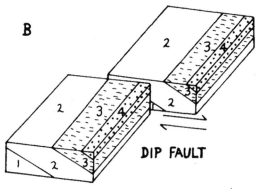

DIP FAULT

BEDS ARE NUMBERED IN SEQUENCE OF DEPOSITION

Great Langdale, eg Stickle Ghyll, and of Hell Gill carved below the south-eastern face of Bow Fell. The most important result of all is that Great Langdale is divided into three sections by these systems: Mickleden, a dip-joint section; the Stool End-Row Head, or Middle section along strike joints; the lower, Chapel Stile-Skelwith Bridge dip-joint section.

The Pleistocene ice moved through the area, gouging the lovely U-shaped valleys sometimes as deep as 1,700ft below the peaks. The trip into Great Langdale by road tells us that once again this is too simple a concept. From the 'soft' country of Ambleside the A593 winds westwards alongside the River Brathay, whose valley is alternately flat and wide or obscured with hummocks of rock and drift. At Skelwith Bridge the B5343 turns into Langdale across a rocky bar past the waterfall of Skelwith Force and overlooks the small Elterwater basin. Beyond Elterwater village another rocky bar cuts partially across the valley at Chapel Stile. It is only from this point that the full open sweep of Great Langdale becomes apparent.

The full length, therefore, becomes an alternation of open basin and narrow gorge section

Fig 50: The Great Langdale Rock Steps

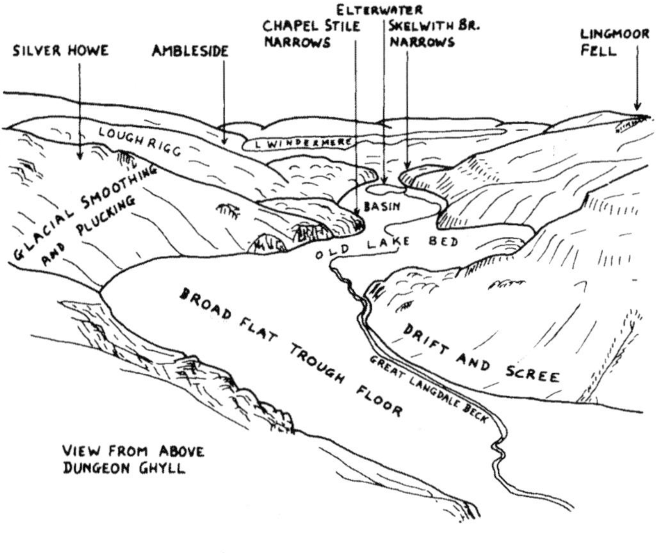

SILVER HOWE   AMBLESIDE   CHAPEL STILE NARROWS   ELTERWATER   SKELWITH BR. NARROWS   LINGMOOR FELL

LOUGH RIGG   L WINDERMERE   GLACIAL SMOOTHING AND PLUCKING   BASIN   OLD LAKE BED

BROAD FLAT TROUGH FLOOR   DRIFT AND SCREE   GREAT LANGDALE BECK

VIEW FROM ABOVE DUNGEON GHYLL

Fig 51: Bow Fell and the Mickleden Trough

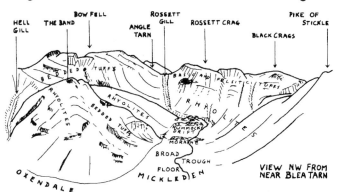

VIEW NW FROM
NEAR BLEA TARN

(Figure 50) which can be explained by the action of the glaciers, the varying structure and rock types. At its maximum the Lake District is believed to have been overrun by ice moving out from a great ice-dome over the Irish Sea, but the glacial effects on the Langdale topography are the result of the work of local ice. Figure 47 indicates the ice-collection centres at the heads of the valleys of Oxendale, Mickleden and Stickle Tarn with further supply from the upper fell surfaces. The main ice-lobe moved down the valley and where conditions of flow changed, as at outcrops of resistant rocks, at variations in gradient, or of ice supply, a rock bar developed under the ice. The Chapel Stile and Skelwith Bridge gorge sections are rock bars (Figure 50).

In the Elterwater basin between the rock bars, the Little Langdale glacier joined the main stream partly via the route followed by the present River Brathay, but mostly over the col at Dale End. This enlarged flow moved east to the present Clappersgate where it was joined by the powerful Rothay ice-stream fed by several tributaries to the north, and so the total flow turned south along the Windermere basin.

We can now put together the effects of geology and weathering processes by examination of the separate sections of the valley. Seen from the Blea Tarn col (289052), Mickleden is a splendid amphitheatre nearly two miles long, its joint-guided alignment being indicated by the fault gully of Rossett Gill (Figure 51). The floor of the valley has a covering of glacial ground moraine overlain by post-glacial detrital and alluvial materials which partially mask the Langdale rhyolites. These last are well exposed along the flanks, including the crags, and across part of The Band. Above these there is a rim of subaqueous Bedded Tuffs and cappings of Wrengill andesitic lavas, the bedding of which can be seen on Bow Fell.

The structure of The Band is interesting (Figure 51). As the diagram shows, the middle segment of the spur is made up of Bedded Tuffs sandwiched between the flanking rhyolites by a sharp infold – part of an isoclinal fold. This is a good indication that the local structure is, in reality, a very wrinkled anticline. The dip of the

Tuffs to the ENE is well exposed on the path which ascends the snout of the Band above Stool End (277057).

The sequence in Oxendale is similar (Figure 52) although the amphitheatre is much more dissected and broken. There is considerable ice-smoothing but Crinkle Gill, Biscoe Beck and others have carved deep gashes into the middle and upper slopes. Their alignment seems to be mainly the result of the joint systems, Crinkle Gill along a strike-joint and Biscoe Beck along a dip-joint, with Hell Gill in particular carved across the rhyolites.

These gashes have several interesting facets. They have clearly been cut since the surrounding slope was smoothed

Fig 52: Upper Oxendale and the Band

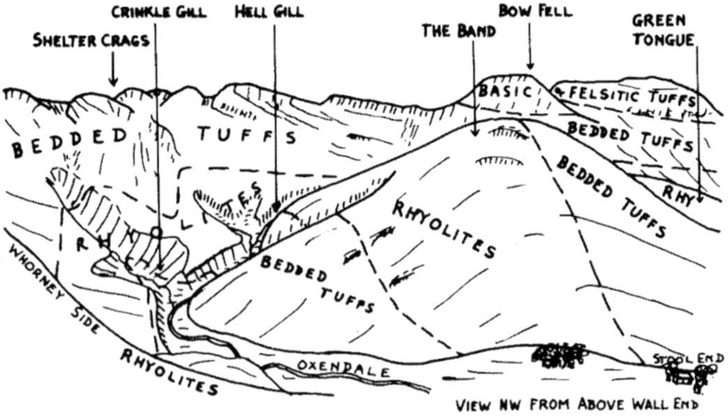

VIEW NW FROM ABOVE WALL END

Fig 53: Simulation of the Oxendale Gully Evolution

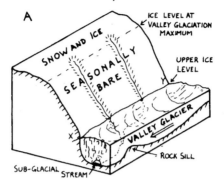

A

ICE LEVEL AT VALLEY GLACIATION MAXIMUM

UPPER ICE LEVEL

SNOW AND ICE

SEASONALLY BARE

VALLEY GLACIER

ROCK SILL

SUB-GLACIAL STREAM

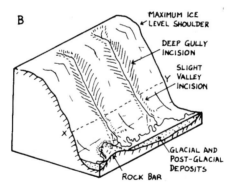

B

MAXIMUM ICE LEVEL SHOULDER

DEEP GULLY INCISION

SLIGHT VALLEY INCISION

GLACIAL AND POST-GLACIAL DEPOSITS

ROCK BAR

by ice, which would suggest that the gullies indicate the amount of post-glacial erosion. However, the incision is much less on the lower slopes, and although this may be due to differential resistance of rocks, a more likely answer is that they originated during a late stage of the valley glaciation (Figure 53). The upper ice limit lay across the lower slope, with snow and ice on the upper surfaces, providing ample meltwater over the seasonally bare middle slopes. Thus, when the ice finally disappeared, perhaps 10,000 years ago, the middle and upper slopes were already partially gullied.

TRANSECT

The well-worn path along Mickleden begins at the Old Dungeon Ghyll Hotel, below Raven Crag (285061). The walk is easy but the valley floor is not so smooth as it appears from afar. The very steep slopes have yielded much detritus and solifluction material until the lower slopes are actually a series of overlapping fans of roughly graded material – sometimes stone chutes and sometimes slumped material of fine matrix with varied fragments. Occasionally the closely jointed Langdale rhyolites appear. These extend upwards to Glimmer Crag where the rocks can be seen to be much more massive than those in the path. The tuffs and andesites of the uppermost slopes and their wide variety are indicated by the confusion of rock types found in the detrital fans – grey, purple, brown, coarse, fine and agglomerate are all to be seen. In addition there are a number of fragments whose weathered surfaces have a distinctive white patina with fresh faces showing a fine grain and a green coloration. This is the famous Langdale Hornstone which was formed by the hardening and baking of fine-grained submarine ashes when the Langdale rhyolites were injected. Thus, the hornstone

Fig 54: The Glacial Trough of Mickelden

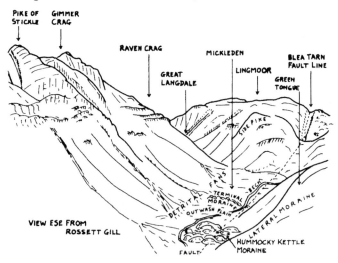

band, up to 50ft in thickness, lies immediately above the rhyolite. Its outcrop can be seen as a lighter band in the upper wall below Pike of Stickle. Its hard flint-like qualities were known to our ancestors, and at the upper end of the stone-filled gully separating Glimmer Crag and Pike of Stickle was a large Neolithic axe-head factory. It is a stiff scramble but worth it for partially worked artefacts can still occasionally be found amid the rubble.

Approximately halfway along Mickleden, a low patch of drift crosses the valley floor (Figure 54). This is a terminal moraine, behind which a very flat section extends to the hummocky kettle drift seen ahead, which is typical of stagnant ice melting away in situ and simply dropping its load to the floor of the valley. Some smoothing and sorting would have been done by the meltwaters, but where present-day streams are cutting this drift the generally unsorted nature can be seen. The flat area between the drift and the terminal moraine may well have been a shallow lakelet and certainly an outwash plain, across which the finer materials from the hummocky drift were sorted and redeposited.

Green Tongue is an interesting spur. Like the others it has been truncated by the valley-glaciers but is now plastered with a deep smoothed mantle of drift, which can be examined in the primary gullies now fretting its surface. It is uncertain whether this is a lateral moraine, deposited along the flank of the moving ice, or a terminal moraine of an ice-tongue from Rossett Gill head.

Standing beside the hummocky drift and gazing around the huge amphitheatre from Bow Fell to Stake Pass, one can realise the volume of snow which could accumulate, change to ice and flow out as supply to the Great Langdale glacier.

Climbing parallel to Rossett Gill, the rhyolite-bedded tuffs junction can be identified (259073) in the jointed and occasionally faulted exposures in the stream banks. The principal interest of the climb is, of course, the Rossett Gill fault shatter zone, which begins where the path crosses to the north bank (254072). This is one of the major faults of the central Lake District, whose path can be followed easily from above Blea Tarn to the back of Great Gable. Its movement has been mainly vertical, hundreds of feet, and there has been some wrenching. Such movements must be associated with friction, drag and various stresses and here we have a classic result – a zone of shattered rock up to 30 yards wide, which has proved far less resistant to weathering processes than the more competent surrounding rocks.

The general rock sequence up the gully is from fine-grained ashes to increasingly coarse tuffs, predominantly andesitic, and even agglomerates, all with various degrees of hardening. Brecciation – the breaking of rocks into fragments by the stresses of the fault movements and the subsequent compaction – is common, noticeable particularly on weathered surfaces which become markedly 'knobbled'. Also very distinctive is the abundant red staining. This is the result of haematite-rich water percolating through the many fissures in the shatter zone. Finally, quartz veining frequently criss-crosses the exposures.

The shattering and hardening complicate field mapping, but the continuous exposures along the walls of the gully do help, and the local dip is away to the north-east. Bedding is seen particularly on weathered faces where the gradation in an individual tuff bed from a coarse base to a finer top, denoting the explosive beginning, and the later settling out of finer material is repeated. Phenocrysts of quartz and felspars become more common in the coarser materials of the upper gully.

Near the col, ice-smoothed outcrops appear to the south of the path, indicating that at least at the higher stages of the glaciation ice from the Angle Tarn corrie overspilled the Rossett Gill col and joined the Langdale glaciers. Above glower the Bow Fell crags where the dip of the Wrengill Andesites and the individual flows are identified. The jointing systems have been worked on by the weathering agencies and have produced the castellated effect. From the col there is a fine view back down the fault line. The steepness of the valley head can be experienced by the pain in the chest from the climb-equalled only by the ache in the knees after the scramble down!

Angle Tarn is a typical corrie lake, set into its ice-deepened basin with the fine headwall of Hanging Knotts cut into a sequence of dark tuffs, whose dip can be seen in the face. The headwall is gashed by a straight gully, indicating another strike-joint line of weakness. The two 'arms' of the corrie armchair are composed of knobs of solid tuffs plastered with dumps of ablation moraines from the final retreat stage when the ice-tongue was restricted to its nivation area. Thus, the coarse unsorted drift is largely of fresh angular material from Hanging Knotts. The outlet is northeastwards to Langstrath (Figure 55) over a drift-masked lip and Langstrath itself is another lovely example of a glaciated trough, the smoothed curves of its flanks, the marked break of slope at the upper limit of the valley glacier,

Fig 55: The Langstrath Glacial Trough

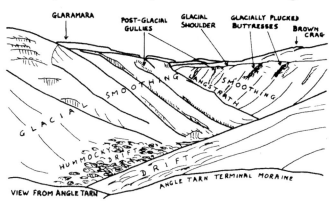

VIEW FROM ANGLE TARN

and the erosion surface above this being the most significant features.

The path to Esk Hause (234081) continues across a series of medium and coarse tuffs and follows the fault line, indicated by the shattering and red staining underfoot. Immediately beyond Angle Tarn is a second hollow (238080), an example of a halfway stage in corrie development – the headwalls shows some steepening and the hollow is partially deepened. There has been, at most, a small tarn and the basin is now marsh, surrounded by hummocky drift. Below the lip, smoothed knobs of rock tell their tale of ice movement out of this hollow.

On the incline to the Esk Hause col, gaily coloured rocks appear in the path. They have a grey matrix with green, purple and red inclusions. The weathered surfaces are purple, pink and white. These are regarded as ignimbrites, the result of a nuée ardente eruption. This explosive episode brought a cloud of poisonous gas and dust rolling across the country, depositing the coarse ash rocks of Esk Hause and denote a period of subaerial deposition. A modern example of nuée ardente was the disaster of Mt Pelee, whose eruption in 1902 destroyed the town of St Pierre on the island of Martinique in a few minutes.

The Esk Hause col (235083) gives a panoramic view across a northerly arc, including the Great Gable ridge, which is composed of a complex succession of tuffs and lava flows. In front of this ridge Styhead Tarn and Sprinkling Tarn are hidden below Seathwaite Fell although the upper section of Borrowdale and Grain Gill can be picked out – the remarkably straight line being one of the N-S faults which fragment the country between Esk Hause and Great Gable. In contrast, the continuing line of the Rossett Gill Fault accounts for the deep gash of Aaron Slack east of Great Gable, the line here being displaced to the north by one of the N-S faults.

To the north-west the gentle erosion surface from the Pikes to Sergeant Man approximates to the dip slope of the Great Langdale scarp and one arm of the syncline mentioned earlier. The syncline is illustrated by the presence of the youngest beds, the Lincomb Tarn Formation, extending over this upper surface from Esk Hause to Glaramara and Sergeant Man.

Away to the south-east the much softer country of the Silurian sedimentary rocks around Lake Windermere contrasts strongly with the Borrowdale Volcanic landscape, and on the horizon the flat-topped Howgill Fells with their fluted sides are equally distinctive.

In the immediate vicinity of Esk Hause the nearest hilltops of Esk Pike, Great End and Allen Crags are capped by the youngest solid series found locally, the Esk Pike Hornstone. Originally a subaqueous fine volcanic dust which settled gently as mud in still water, this has been hardened by later movements and nearby intrusions to the present flinty greenish rock which weathers to the grey or white patina. Examples can be obtained along the footpath to Esk Pike summit.

A path continues from Esk Pike to Bow Fell summit via the fault-controlled Ore Gap (241072) and most of the traverse is across a sequence of moderately dipping medium-to-coarse tuff beds, usually grey to dark grey, andesitic in character, but at the Ore Gap col the masses of rubble contain porphyritic and brecciated rocks which are often stained purple. This is believed to be a 'vent agglomerate', that is, the remains of a volcanic vent up which the magmatic materials passed. The upper part of the vent has been removed and no local lava flows have been identified positively with this vent. There are concentrations of haematite sufficiently large to have been worked during the eighteenth century, and the remains of an old shaft is found a few yards NNE of the footpath. The iron ore was taken by packpony to a furnace in Langstrath.

From Ore Gap to Bow Fell summit and over to Three Tarns (249061), there is a fine sequence of Bedded Tuffs showing grading within beds. The effects of

Fig 56: The Mighty Crags of Scafell

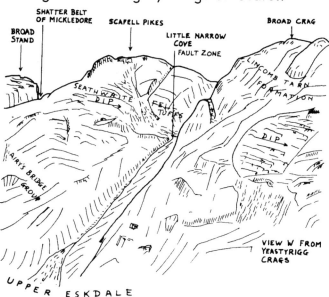

weathering agencies working on the joint systems in this very exposed, almost subarctic environment where little vegetation has been able to establish itself, is seen by the masses of shattered rock littering the upper surfaces. To the west lies the fault valley of Yeastyrigg Gill and the scarp crags beyond. The western horizon is dominated by the Scafell Pikes (Figure 56) upon whose crags the great thickness of medium and coarse tuffs of the Seathwaite Fell Series stand out. Corrie hollows nestle into these crags, once providing ice for the Eskdale glacier. This whole section on Bow Fell provides excellent views across the Langdale region, and if the wind drops sufficiently an overview of the relationships between geology and topography can be obtained by the use of geological and topographic maps.

The return to the Old Dungeon Ghyll Hotel is completed by the ridge path down The Band, where the rock sequence is followed in reverse to the Langdale rhyolites. The middle section of Great

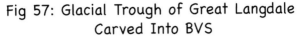

Fig 57: Glacial Trough of Great Langdale Carved Into BVS

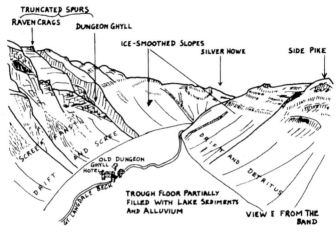

Langdale – the strike-joint section cut out of the arch of the anticline – opens out during this descent, the steep crags forming scarps which dip away to north and south (Figure 57). The intricate network of field walls are of eighteenth-century origin, suggesting a period of enclosure, improvement and prosperity.

The considerable late glacial and post-glacial infilling of the valley floor is evident: ground moraine against the solid rock, then meltwater or lake deposits and finally post-glacial alluvium of the present stream, whose course is now largely culverted. This culverting, completed in 1971, has been done most beautifully in the local style – layers of the grey, rounded stream cobbles interlain with levels of flat flags of the slate beds.

The deep gashes into the north side, cut by Dungeon Ghyll and Stickle Ghyll along dip joints, contain tumbling 'forces' or waterfalls over the massive rhyolites. Paths ascend each gorge and although the climbs are steep there are continuous exposures across the Langdale rhyolites, the tuffs and occasional lava flows above and the junction once more being indicated by the white-surfaced hornstone.

Stickle Tarn (Figure 58) occupies another corrie hollow with its near-vertical headwall of Pavey Ark.

Jointing is massive and the whole section is of tuffs, mostly andesitic and fairly coarse. There is one diagonal crack which is a favourite route for a ropeless 'scramble'. Hummocky moraines surround the tarn, but there is an extensive amphitheatre floored and flanked by rock-knobs partially smothered with drift, giving a strange knobbly appearance. The ice-masses melted in situ here and the unsorted drift remained. To the north Sergeant Man projects, composed of the youngest local beds – the Lincomb Tarn Beds – preserved in the syncline to the north of Langdale.

The broad open character of Great Langdale continues along the dip-joint direction south-eastwards to the rock bar at Chapel Stile where the resistant felsitic Bedded Tuffs, metamorphosed to slates, have replaced the intrusive rhyolites in the valley floor. These hard, green and grey-green slates have been extensively quarried for several hundred years as the many spoil heaps breaking through the scrub and woodland indicate. Thrang Quarry (317055), beside the road at Chapel Stile, is typical: the fine-to-medium ashes have been subjected to low-grade metamorphism by crustal pressures which have produced hardening and cleavage. The original bedding can still be seen in some faces, giving the lovely banded effect of certain ornamental slates. The cleavage is usually

Fig 58: Corrie Headwall of Stickle Tarn

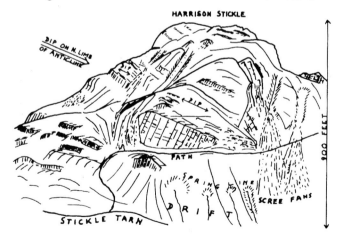

89

at a high angle to the bedding. Many disturbed rocks show some cleavage but it is the regularity of the cleavage planes and the hardness of the rocks which have made these particularly profitable commercially. This is the eastern end of the famous arc of commercial slate which stretches south-westwards past Coniston to Ulpha. The present trend away from slates for roofing has meant a decline in slate production, but there is still a strong market for ornamental slates. Its beauty as a building material is well illustrated in the new Catholic church at Grasmere which is built of green slates.

Elterwater lake itself is a remnant of a once larger water body now heavily silted up. The disappearance of the lake above Chapel Stile and the reduction of Elterwater has been caused partially by the silting and partially by the cutting of the gorges across the impounding rock bars at Chapel Stile and Skelwith Force which has lowered the outlet points and hence the water level behind the outlets.

The settlements of Elterwater and Chapel Stile, once dependent primarily upon slate, are now prospering under the tourist boom. Many fine pieces of slate may still be collected during walks through the now wooded spoil-heaps of Elterwater Quarries south of the village. The minor road past these quarries runs through the ice-cut col through which the Little Langdale ice moved to join the Great Langdale tongue at Elterwater, whose basin is terminated by the upstanding rock bar at Skelwith Bridge.

Chapter 6

The South-Eastern Lake District

THIS SEGMENT of the Lake District is a series of valleys and intervening uplands radiating from the mountain knot of High Street (441111, Figure 59). With the exception of Troutbeck in the extreme west none of the valleys has a through road, and some are scarcely penetrated by a surfaced lane. In consequence, despite their proximity to Kendal and the principal access routes to the region, these are some of the least-visited valleys. The most popular is Haweswater which bounds the area on the north, for a road penetrates to the head of the Manchester Corporation reservoir (469108) and gives access to some of the finest glaciated scenery of the Lake District in the cwms containing Blea Water (448108) and Small Water (455100), whose paths lead on to the high level erosion surface of High Street.

Geologically, interest centres upon the contrasting scenery developed on different rock types, for the northern half of the district is built upon the BVS while the southern half is on the Silurian sedimentary formations which dominate the southern third of the Lake District. Both series follow the characteristic ENE-WSW trend in their basic structure. Once more

the BVS provides the rugged terrain while the Silurian mudstones, shales and grits have been moulded to a softer topography, generally below 1,700ft OD. In addition there is the Shap Granite intrusion and its metamorphic aureole, possibly the best known of the major Devonian intrusions and certainly the most accessible and observable in the large quarries alongside the A6 (558083 and 565106). Geomorphologically, the principal controlling agents have been the ice-sheets and the valley-glaciers which spilled out radiating tongues of ice from the ice-collection grounds on and around the High Street massif.

This chapter takes in three localities to illustrate this varied geology and scenery: Longsleddale, which illustrates the BVS-Silurian contrasts; Haweswater, with its magnificent glacial scenery; and the Shap Granite intrusion and metamorphic aureole.

LONGSLEDDALE

This long, straight glacial trough down which now flows the River Sprint, penetrates seven miles into the upland massif from Garnett Bridge (523992) to the southern flank of Harter Fell (460093), the first five miles as far as Sadgill (482057) possessing a surfaced

Fig 59: SE Lake District - Physical Framework

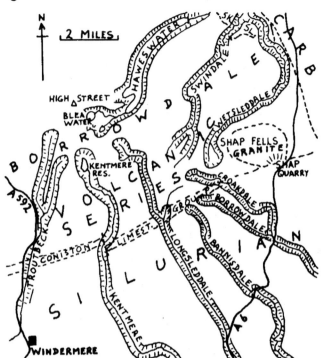

lane. Almost to Sadgill hamlet the valley is cut into Silurian rocks. These are seen first in a small quarry at the lane junction with the A6 above Garnett Bridge (526987). The rock is Bannisdale Slate, the principal member of the Silurian succession which may total 5,000ft in this locality. It is a fine-grained mudstone, varying grey in colour, with steep dip and strong, if irregular, cleavage.

The considerable thickness of Silurian sedimentary rocks is the result of some forty million years of sedimentation in seas which oscillated in level and in which the location of the shoreline and hence the source of material for sedimentation varied although the

Table 4: The Silurian Succession in the Southern Lake District

Series	Formation	Character	Approx Thickness (ft)
	Passing upwards into the Devonian desert sandstones		
Ludlow	Kirkby Moor Flags	Arenaceous: sandstones and siltstones, with calcareous fossil-bearing lenses	1,400–2,800
	Bannisdale Slates	Argillaceous: banded dark, grey mudstones with lighter siltstone bands	4,700
	Coniston Grits	Arenaceous: greywackes, grey and brown	2,300–5,200
	Upper Coldwell Beds	Arenaceous: coarse flags; grey graptolitic mudstones and some siltstones	20–1,400
Wenlock	Middle Coldwell Beds	Argillaceous: calcareous siltstones and mudstones, limestones. Fossiliferous	20–400
	Lower Coldwell Beds	⎱ Arenaceous: greywackes and grits, within the Brathay Flags ⎰	
	Brathay Flags	Mainly argillaceous: dark bluish-grey muddy siltstones, frequently graptolitic	1,300
Llandovery	Stockdale Shales–Browgill Beds	Argillaceous: grey-green non-graptolitic mudstones, with darker mudstones and occasional ash bands	280
	Skelgill Beds	Argillaceous: black, carbonaceous, graptolitic mudstones, with included grey mudstones	60–110
	Conformable passage from Ordovician Ashgill Shales of the Coniston Limestone Group		

Fig 60: Generalised Silurian Succession along West Flank of Longsleddale

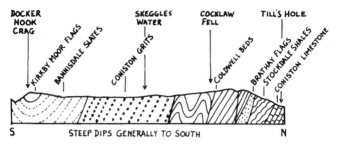

main landmass remained to the north. The outcome is an alternation of argillaceous formations, eg mudstones and shales, deposited in periods of quiet, deep waters, often far from the shore, and arenaceous deposits, eg sandstones and grits, indicating the proximity of the shoreline and an abundance of detritus, including coarse material. This alternating succession is summarised in Table 4.

(i) Docker Nook-Till's Hole

From Garnett Bridge to Docker Nook (505013) the valley and its surrounding uplands are underlain by Bannisdale Slates, but from the latter farm two miles NNW to Till's Hole (485051) it is possible to follow the Silurian succession from the youngest formation, the Kirkby Moor Flags on Docker Nook Crags, to the oldest beds, the basement Stockdale Shales at

the Till's Hole col to Stile End (468049, Figure 60).

The Kirkby Moor Flags are well exposed on Docker Nook Crags directly NW from the farm. They are preserved in the core of the Bannisdale syncline, one of the larger-scale flexures trending ENE-WSW across the district. The formation is here incomplete, the outcrop being less than 400 yards wide, barely half that to the west in Kentmere. The dips vary from 30° to near-vertical, predominantly to the SSE and S. The conditions of sedimentation were of a steadily disappearing sea with the approach of the Devonian desert era. The beds became increasingly arenaceous, although shelly, and calcareous lenses, indicative of temporary locally clear waters, do occur in some localities. The common rock form is a brown medium grit with well-spaced joints.

As one emerges above Docker Nook Crags, boggy gently rolling country stretches away to Skeggles Water (480033). This section of the country illustrates how part of the Lake District scenery is made up of a series of erosion surface remnants associated with former sea-levels, these remnants being separated by distinct breaks of slope (Figure 61). In the south-east Lake District six such remnant surfaces have been identified, three of which occur across these fells west of Longsleddale. The highest, over 1,250ft OD, stretches from Docker Nook Crags in an arc to Staveley Head Fell (475017) and is one of the lowest sections of the 'Red Screes' surface, whose most common occurrence is 1,500-l,800ft. This makes the important

Fig 61: Erosion Surface Remnants in Longsleddale

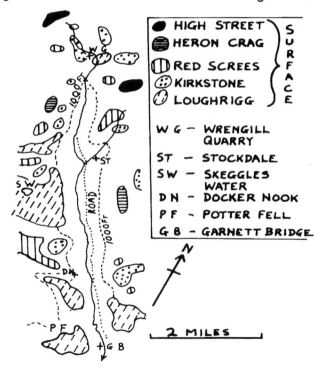

HIGH STREET ⎫
HERON CRAG ⎪
RED SCREES ⎬ SURFACE
KIRKSTONE ⎪
LOUGHRIGG ⎭

W G — WRENGILL QUARRY
ST — STOCKDALE
SW — SKEGGLES WATER
D N — DOCKER NOOK
P F — POTTER FELL
G B — GARNETT BRIDGE

N

2 MILES

point that these surfaces are by no means level, but are best thought of as rolling landscapes with a regional slope towards the shoreline of those long-past seas. Thus, most of the erosion surfaces have been plotted through altitude ranges in excess of 300ft.

The second remnant is a bench athwart Kilnstone Gill across which the stream meanders above the wood at around 1,050-1,150ft OD. A second flat is seen along the east side of Cocklaw Fell (482040). These are part of the 'Kirkstone Surface' (1,100-1,400ft OD). The third level, part of the 'Loughrigg Surface', at 750-900ft OD, but up to 1,100ft OD locally, is by far the most extensive, partly the result of it being the most recent. It can be seen to the south of Docker Nook across the shoulders of Tenter Howe (508008) and Potter Fell above Garnett Bridge. The largest remnant stretches across the shallow basin in which Skeggles Water lies. Our transect crosses patches of all these surfaces and it will become evident that locally the divisions between the levels are not well defined.

Immediately north of Docker Nook Crags the Bannisdale Slates reappear on the northern limb of the syncline and extend for more than a mile across Sleddale Forest. The syncline is itself crumpled by small-scale folds, down to a few inches in size. These are difficult to find locally as most of the minor folds have long limbs dipping steeply SSE, ie in the normal regional direction, and it is the short, moderately dipping NNW limbs which give the clue to their interpretation. The dark, often graptolitic mudstones are interspersed with pale siltstone laminations giving this formation its distinctive banded appearance, which has the advantage of picking out the small-scale folding – compare the much older Skiddaw Slates of the northern Lake District in which the argillaceous members have proved much less competent than the arenaceous formations and crumple more easily.

Although in no locality is the structure of the Silurian sedimentaries as complex as that of the Skiddaw Slates, there is still controversy about the structure. It seems certain that the lower formations, below the Coniston Grits, are merely steeply dipping limbs and that any more complex folding is to be found in the argillaceous Bannisdale Slates. However, if folding even in these upper formations is fairly simple, as in the Docker Nook syncline, then a total thickness approaching 5,000ft is possible, as indicated in Table 4. If the folding is more severe, repetition of beds may result and a much thinner sequence is likely, eg many of the beds in the

Bannisdale Slates are remarkably similar. This complex structure underlying ragged terrain recurs across Kentmere and westwards from Coniston Water.

Amid the generally peaty nature of the terrain there are a surprising number of minor solid outcrops, indicating the effectiveness of ice in scouring an upland surface. Yet there are numbers of boulders scattered about which today show excellent examples of the work of mechanical processes such as frost-thaw in cracking and disintegrating quite large blocks. There is no path along the transect and it is most useful to walk near the eastern edge in order to look down into Longsleddale, although Beech Hill Wood and the nature of the valley shoulder impede the views.

The first landmark is Flew Scar (491036), a crag overlooking Longsleddale above Hollin Root Farm (493034). North of Black Beck a careful watch on the outcrops underfoot will note the change to a coarser facies approximately along the line of old shooting boxes, indicating that we have passed downwards into the Coniston Grits. Once again the dips are generally steep to the south,

Fig 62: Contrasting Scenery Around Stockdale

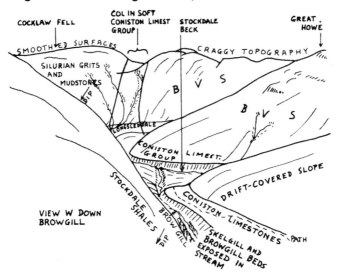

with occasional reversals denoting folding. This formation, well shown on Flew Scar, consists typically of grey and brown greywacke grits with jointing from massive to fracture cleavage, which produces flaggy blocks. In the lower beds there are some argillaceous bands within which a few graptolites may be found, but exposures of such bands are poor.

The Coniston Grits continue for some three quarters of a mile until the line of the gill along the northern edge of Underhill Wood (487042), the coarse fossiliferous sandstones of the basal beds being observable in the small outcrops west of the wood (485042). Through several of the localities at which the Coniston Grit–Coldwell beds junction is observable, there is evidence of a discontinuity or thrust near the junction, but here on Cocklaw Fell there is no easily seen field evidence. The Coldwell Beds are an alternating succession of mudstones, sandstone and grits running across the northern flank of Cocklaw Fell. The first group observable are the grey calcareous siltstones and mudstones of the Middle Coldwell Beds, seen occasionally in the gills running south of Hill Cottage (489046). The Lower Coldwell Beds are here thin beds of greywackes within the 1,200ft of the Brathay Flags and are not easily identifiable. There is

a series of discontinuous exposures in the stream which flows to Till's Hole. More easily seen is the arrival of the argillaceous Skelgill Beds of the Stockdale Shales (485049). As one follows the stream, the outcrops of relatively easily erodable Stockdale Shales and the Coniston Limestones can be seen in the low col to Stile End and eastwards across the valley to the Stockdale re-entrant (Figure 62). North of the col the crags south of Sadgill Wood signify the incoming of the BVS.

(ii) Stockdale-Browgill

The basal members of the Silurian succession were detailed as early as 1888 by Professor Nicholson in his transect up Browgill Beck from Stockdale (491053), thereby establishing one of the classic geological sites of the Lake District. This valley-head hamlet has dwindled to a single farm plus an outdoor-pursuits centre, and is the point at which the Haweswater aqueduct emerges from its five mile tunnel.

The Stockdale Shales are subdivisible into two subformations, the Skelgill Beds, up to 110ft of dark graptolitic mudstones, but not well seen here, and the Browgill Beds whose main beds are present. (A classic locality for the Browgill Beds is above Banishead Quarry (278960) in the Coniston valley.)

Fig 63: The Stockdale Shales at Brow Gill

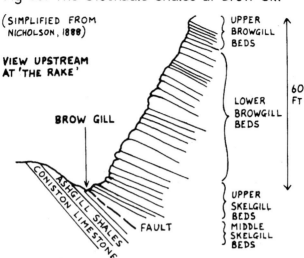

(SIMPLIFIED FROM NICHOLSON, 1888)

VIEW UPSTREAM AT 'THE RAKE'

BROW GILL

CONISTON LIMESTONE

ASHGILL SHALES

FAULT

UPPER BROWGILL BEDS

LOWER BROWGILL BEDS

60 FT

UPPER SKELGILL BEDS

MIDDLE SKELGILL BEDS

Immediately above Stockdale Farm the dark Brathay Flags, with occasional pale-green mudstones are exposed in the stream bed below the massive lime kiln and the Haweswater aqueduct. Between the lime kiln and the base of the waterfall a succession of pale green or purple shales with occasional pale grit bands dip at approximately 60° to the SSE, their surfaces freshened but often darkened by water. After a glimpse of the dark basal Skelgill Beds, the waterfall itself is built on the dark muddy Coniston Limestone, a good example of how impure limestones may be, and how unlike the 'typical' pale-grey examples. This is the passage into the Ordovician strata, a discontinuity being produced by a thrust or low-angle fault. The dark calcareous mudstones continue to outcrop above the junction with Browgill (492055) in a deeply cut cleft assisted by the blocky jointing system. As the open fell begins, the hard, often pink, Stockdale Rhyolite forms the cascades over which the Stockdale Beck tumbles. This acid quartz-rich lava flow spilled out on the ocean floor as the dying gasp of the Ordovician volcanic episode and is sandwiched between the two sedimentary sections of the Coniston Limestone

Group. Careful examination along the stream will locate, near a group of gnarled thorn bushes (492057), the change from the rhyolite to a' gritty rock which is the basal grit of the sedimentary sequence. It is succeeded upslope-and preceded in time by the BVS proper, in this case the Upper Andesites.

Brow Gill, which joins Stockdale Beck at the waterfall, is a beautiful example of a strike stream (Figure 63), the waters tumbling along the strike, cutting a deep cleft and exposing the scarp and dip of the beds which vary from a few inches to 10ft and which range from a shaly fracture system to a massive appearance. From the junction for 200 yards to approximately the 1,000ft contour Coniston Limestone is exposed, but with debris of the Stockdale Rhyolite in the bed and amid the drift in the banks. The Limestone is faulted out (494057) by a small cross fault, which throws the beds a few yards to the north, and the Stockdale Shales come in.

The Coniston Limestone-Stockdale Shales junction is a thrust fault caused by pressures from the south. The deeply cut, somewhat asymmetrical V-shaped valley follows this thrust and the strike. The northern flank of the valley along which the path runs is built along the dip of the Coniston Limestones, and the upper flank

on the pale Stockdale Rhyolite. The exposures are quickly buried beneath a mantle of heavy clay and stone drift, with peat developing further upslope.

The stream cuts along the upper Skelgill Beds, dark graptolitic shales up to 18 inches in each bed. Through these beds runs the thrust fault, indicated by some shattering. The clearest evidence of the discontinuity is the difference in dip between the beds on either bank: on the north bank the dips are approximately 60°, while the beds which ascend the south bank sit at 30-40° (Figure 63). This southern flank exposes the Browgill Beds, 40ft of pale grits and mudstones, greens, fawns and greys, with occasional dark beds. The best exposure is still that used by Nicholson, a steep-sided ravine known as The Rake (497058). This series of beds may be examined in detail and such a study will illustrate how the environmental conditions varied at the time the sediments were deposited: slight changes in load type brought down by streams, changes in sea-level, currents, temperatures etc all caused small but identifiable differences in the resulting rock type. A particularly vivid illustration is given by the variation in animal life suggested by the fossil remains, for most of the beds are barren, but some of the thin dark mudstones contain graptolite remains.

(iii) Upper Longsleddale

North of Stockdale the scenery changes abruptly as the BVS are introduced, here approximately 4,000ft in thickness (Figure 64). The NNW-SSE fault which guides upper Longsleddale throws the succession on the eastern side northwards, but does not disturb the general ENE-WSW strike. The formations lie on the southern limb of the great anticline whose axis runs through Kentmere (445080) and the Nan Bield Pass (455097), caused by pressures from the south-east. As in most of the BVS structures, the highly competent formations have been gently flexed along this limb; but in a belt some two miles wide from Great Howe (489062) to Adam Seat (471091) there is a zone of what has been suggested as more intense folding. Not all geologists would agree with this interpretation, but the proposition is that there is a series of anticlines or isoclines, overturned to the north and truncated by subsequent erosion (Figure 65). Such a proposal helps to account for the recurrent outcrop of the Kentmere Rhyolites which lie below the Wrengill Andesites, for such a structure would preserve them in the cores of eroded anticlines. Certainly the western

flank of Longsleddale below Goat Scar (477070) and Raven Crag (474077) is built of a series of thick lavas, dipping steadily to the south and which are clearly truncated by erosion. To establish the validity of such a proposition detailed field examination would be required along two main lines (a) to discover whether any beds are repeated and (b) to discover whether any beds are inverted.

The folding is further complicated by cross faulting, especially on the eastern side of the valley where the striking mass of Buckbarrow Crag (485073) is segmented, the faults often traceable as gullies, separating rhyolites, andesites and coarse tuffs.

The track from Sadgill crosses lateral moraine partially covered with post-glacial screes and solifluction deposits. The complex solid geological sequence can be followed in general terms from the path by the dominant rock type in the debris underfoot. The Coarse Tuffs of Sadgill are made up of lithic fragments of andesite up to 12 inches across, plus variable pink felsite fragments. They are massive, resistant and usually form rugged country. These are followed upvalley by an alternation of dark Wrengill Andesites and paler Kentmere Rhyolites past the glowering Buckbarrow Crags. The faulting of this hill mass is seen

Fig 64:
Upper Longsleddale - Generalised BVS Geology

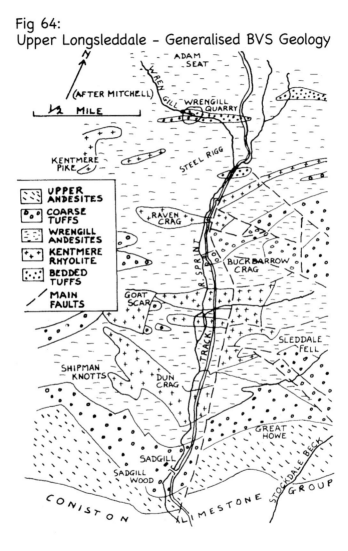

Fig 65: Highly Simplified Impression of the Possible Structure Along W Flank of Upper Longsleddale

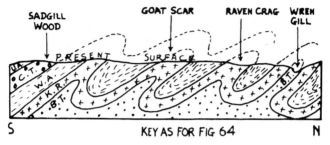

by the frequent quartz veining, eg beside the track as it turns sharply to ascend the trough end (478079). To the west the northerly pointing lava flows of Goat Scar and Raven Crag form impressive cliffs with vertical jointing systems, and are fringed by extensive screes.

The Wrengill Andesites are usually blue-green, aphanitic lavas, often vesicular. Flow-brecciation is common at the base and the top of flows, this brecciation often being distinguishable by its purple coloration. Chlorite and calcite are the result of alteration to the mineral constituents since original solidification, eg these features are well seen in the exposures immediately north of Sadgill Wood.

The Kentmere Rhyolites, with higher silica content than the andesites, are purple to grey, generally fine-grained, but occasionally porphyritic in a glassy groundmass. Their most distinctive feature is the platy jointing system, parallel fractures some 2-3 inches apart, eg the southern flanks of Buckbarrow.

The section of the valley which ascends steeply from the trough end is heavily clogged with morainic drift, on top of which active screes are still being built below some impressive stone chutes which follow the major vertical jointing systems. Some of the huge blocks are 'perched' blocks, left on the moraine by the melting ice, while others are tumbled blocks from the crags above. The young River Sprint has cut a fine gorge and cascades over debris and solid rock. In some of the massive Wrengill Andesites the waters have produced deep swirl hollows, where a stone has been whirled round in a hollow by the force of the water to gradually grind its way deep into the rock, forming a smooth round hole. These holes are seen particularly well in periods of low water.

Towards the top of the steep ascent, the massive lavas give way to an increasingly cleaved succession of fine tuffs composed predominantly of tiny fragments of andesite. These are the typical Bedded Tuffs, which yield the commercial slates – fine-grained, regularly cleaved, pale grey to green. The spoil-heaps first appear at the entrance to the upper basin, but the main quarries follow an E-W gully (476086). The high-angle cleavage, roughly parallel to the strike and to Wrengill, has permitted the working of the quarry westwards into the hill. To the east the cleaved zone passes across the ice-worked Mosedale col. Many of the Wrengill slates are distinctive by their spherulites, small pale speckles of coarser materials partially moulded into oval shapes generally less than an inch in length. Amid the spoil-heaps there are considerable remains of the buildings, equipment and the man-made water conduits which fed the plant.

A splendid overview of the quarries and the full sweep of Longsleddale is obtained from Steel Riggs south of the quarries (475084). The upper basin was

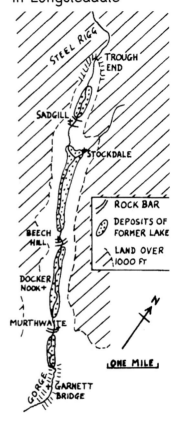

Fig 66: Glacial Lakes in Longsleddale

STEEL RIGG
TROUGH END
SADGILL
STOCKDALE
BEECH HILL
DOCKER NOOK
MURTHWAITE
GORGE
GARNETT BRIDGE

ROCK BAR
DEPOSITS OF FORMER LAKE
LAND OVER 1000 FT

ONE MILE

N

once the névé collecting ground, and is now the gathering ground for the Sprint headwaters. It is crossed by the cleaved belt but is plastered with hummocky drift from the final melting of the last glaciation, over which a layer of peat is developing. This is succeeded by the steep cascade section with its moraine and scree, to be followed by a flat-floored basin to the Sadgill moraine, and on to the succeeding basins.

Having travelled the full length of Longsleddale and now looking back it becomes clear that the valley resembles a string of beads – a series of flat-floored basins separated by narrow, often rocky sections (Figure 66). Each of the basins was once the site of a lake fed by glacial meltwaters ponded back behind rock bars and stage moraines, and drained as the exit levels through these barriers were lowered. Sadgill is the uppermost constriction behind which lies the silt-filled basin now etched into terraces by the post-glacial stream (Figure 67). The second lake was held up by the Beech Hill chapel moraine (Figure 68) and stretched back to Stockdale. The lower flanks are fringed by lateral moraines across which the road winds and on which some of the farms sit, eg Wad's Howe Farm (496031), below the steep slopes and above the floodable valley floor. A third basin extends to near Murthwaite (514008) where a small gorge drops into a fourth, small basin, which gradually fades into the deep Garnett Bridge gorge.

Fig 67: Longsleddale Glacial Trough

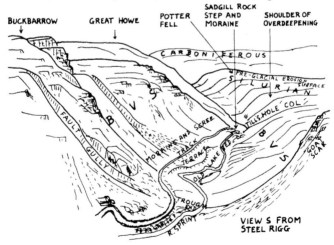

Fig 68: Glacial Features at Beech Hill Longsleddale

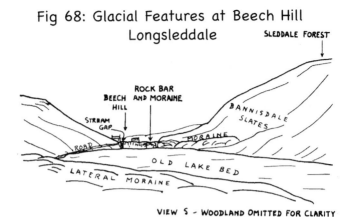

VIEW S - WOODLAND OMITTED FOR CLARITY

From the upper basin of Longsleddale paths radiate eastwards into Mosedale, northwards over the Gatesgarth Pass (474094) to the head of Haweswater, or westwards to The Knowe and Harter Fell (462095). This last route ascends the higher slopes of the Wren Gill basin where the peat layer is sometimes broken

Fig 69: Corries at the Head of Haweswater

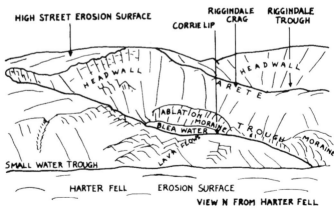

VIEW N FROM HARTER FELL

to reveal the strong drift and gravity debris veneering the solid rock even at this high level. From the wind-ripped and débris-strewn summit erosion surface, generally above 2,300ft OD and cut across Harter Fell Andesites, there are fine views to Kentmere with the half-formed corrie amphitheatre below Ill Bell (435078). To the north-west and north the magnificent assemblage of corrie-hollows, tarns and arêtes at the head of the Haweswater trough are laid out (Figure 69). This cluster of corries is comparable with the group cut into the Coniston Range above Church Beck.

HAWESWATER

The Haweswater valley is approached by the minor road to Bampton and Haweswater, which leaves the A6 at the north end of Shap village (562157). At first the road twists between pale drystone walls, which are built of the splendid Knipe Scar Limestones of the Carboniferous Limestone series. The road passes diagonally up the dip slope of these tilted sedimentaries and after a mile or so emerges on to the scarp crest. To the north large limestone quarries are disfiguring the crest, although the forest cap of Knipe Scar itself remains untouched. It is easy to visualise from this locality the continuation of the thick limestones westwards over the Lake District massif.

From the scarp crest the ground drops away steeply in a series of steps representing the descending succession below the Knipe Scar Limestones to the Lowther valley. This depression has been cut largely into the most southerly and easterly exposure of the Ordovician Skiddaw Slates. The topography around Bampton (521180) is underlain by these slates, but they are generally masked by drift and alluvium. As around Ullswater (Chapter 4) they form soft low country when compared to the succeeding BVS, the junction being similar – a low-angle thrust plane along which the BVS have been shifted.

Beyond Bampton the country is built upon the BVS outcrop. The axis of the Nan Bield anticline noted earlier as running ENE from Kentmere across the Nan Bield col continues over Mardale Banks (481122) and east of Naddle Forest (500145). Thus, the dips of the lava flows and ash bands along Haweswater are generally NW on the northern limb of the anticline. In addition, the locality is crossed by faults, commonly NNW-SSE, eg that which controls the near-vertical west wall of Wallow Crag (469149) on the south flank of Haweswater.

The rock types are dominated by the Nan Bield and Upper Andesites, between which are sandwiched some rhyolitic flows, eg east of Wallow Crag and across Birkhouse Hill (448165) to the north of the lake. The landscape of the corries west of the lake head is built on alternating lava flows and tuff bands including some coarse materials. Across the middle section of the lake are exposures of basic doleritic rocks, which have been called Haweswater Dolerite. This may have been a simple stock intruded into the BVS soon after the occurrence of the lavas, but recent workers have not mapped this separately from the BVS in general. It outcrops on both sides of the lake although the woods of the southern flank obscure the exposures. As seen on Wallow Crag it varies in type from yellowish with a low ferromagnesian content of some 10 per cent to a dark, blue-black, more basic, ferromagnesian-rich (36 per cent) type. Texture ranges from fine to coarse and the contacts with the surrounding country rock are variable.

Haweswater lake was originally much smaller, attaining a level of 695ft OD, ringed by a farming community and almost divided by the extensive delta erected by the vigorous Measand Beck. From 1926 the Manchester City reservoir has raised the level to above 800ft lengthening and broadening the lake but wiping out the farms, eg walls can still be seen disappearing into the lake.

The National Plan of the Water Resources Board, published in January 1974, envisages the raising of the level at least a further 100ft. Even with the partial inundation, the glacial origins of the trough remain clear (Figure 70) with the classic shoulder of overdeepening, smoothing of the flanks and overall U-shape. This principal valley-glacier was fed by four ice-collection hollows which developed during the Ice Age to large corries from which ice-tongues spilled, eg Riggindale, Blea Water, Small Water and Gatesgarth.

The road and the lake terminate at a trough end (469108), a point where the junction of two side glaciers gave greater downward erosive power to the combined ice, thereby overdeepening the trough. From the car park three of the tributary troughs can be seen, the glacial lips shielding Small Water, and Blea Water being particularly impressive. Follow the path towards Small Water and the steepness of what was once an ice-fall can be appreciated, the stream cascading down successive lava flows. The first section of the path passes over hummocky drift, which, with marshy post-glacial alluvium, fills the trough floor above the lake. This drift is fresh and is material dumped by the melting of the final 'mini-glaciation' less than 9,000 years

Fig 70: The Small Water Corrie

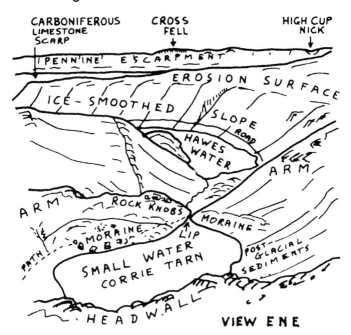

ago. Similar deposits may be seen in upper Langdale and the Seathwaite valley.

Corrie, or coire, is the Scottish term for an armchair-shaped hollow in mountains, which is the product of freeze-thaw action coupled with the action of small glaciers. The Welsh term cwm and the French cirque are also in common usage.

Well-developed corries consist of three distinct morphological elements (Figure 71). First there are steep near-vertical headwalls and sidewalls usually of shattered appearance. Second are concave floors, often showing evidence of smoothing and polishing, which meet the head walls at a sharp break of slope. Third there are lips and thresholds at the corrie entrances which may consist of bedrock, glacial moraine or a combination of the two. Such lips frequently impound lakes or tarns.

Corries occur either at the heads of glacial troughs, as in the cluster around the head of Haweswater, or as discrete forms cut into the flanks of glacial valleys, eg Burtness Comb above Buttermere (Chapter 7), and both types originate in previously watereroded depressions. They show a preferred orientation, being best developed on NE facing slopes. Such an orientation gives maximum shade, hence maximum snow accumulation, and a generally leeside location in Britain, which assists collection for although the windward slopes receive heavier amounts, the snow is accumulated less readily.

These hollows are best developed and preserved in resistant rocks such as the BVS and vary widely in size, but clearly some considerable erosive power is applied for the largest British example is more than half a mile across, some 1,500ft deep and involved the removal of 700 million metric tons of bedrock! Controversy lingers concerning their origin and centres around two aspects – the great height of some headwalls and the overdeepening of corrie floors. There is general agreement that development consists of two stages. First is the development of depressions beneath the snow patches, which collect in preglacial hollows. The hollows are then enlarged by nivation, ie a combination of freeze-thaw, solifluction and wash, to become nivation hollows. As the hollows achieve a certain critical depth, pressure at their bases is sufficient to turn the snow to firn and eventually ice. Second, once a corrie has its ice-mass, subsequent enlargement is the product of glacial erosion, ie downwasting of the corrie floor and freeze-thaw action, which extends the corrie laterally to provide the 'sole' (underside) of the glacier with the tools to erode as it moves.

It is with this second stage that the problems lie, the theories being grouped into the Bergschrund Hypothesis and the Meltwater Hypothesis. The former was first proposed in 1904 and claims that the diurnal freezing and thawing at the base of the large crevasse or bergschrund, commonly found in the upper part of a corrie glacier and extending down to the bedrock, would result in the sapping of the headwall. The shattered debris is then incorporated into the glacier as bed load for further erosion (Figure 71). This seems beautifully simple but is open to several objections, the principal ones being that bergschrunds are not always found in modem corrie-glaciers and that because of pressures and plastic yielding of the ice, the crevasses are unlikely to remain open at depths greater than 150ft.

Finally, measurements have indicated that the required

amplitude of temperature changes at the base of the bergschrund simply do not occur, cold air sinking to create relatively stable conditions.

The Meltwater Hypothesis (1960) proposes that meltwater is able to stream down the headwall between the rock and the ice (this gap is called the 'randkluft') permitting freeze-thaw action to take place over much of the headwall surface enabling relatively rapid destruction (Figure 71). This contrasts with

Fig 71: Corrie Formation

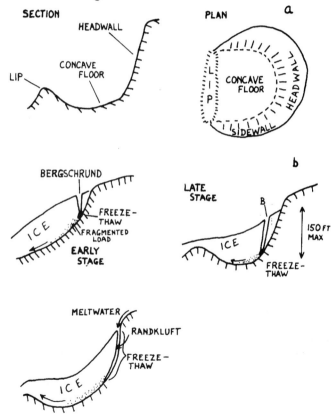

Fig 72:
Theories of Ice Movement in Corrie Glaciers

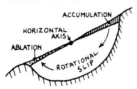

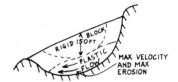

the bergschrund concept, which would concentrate any action in a narrow strip at the base of the crevasse. Destruction may be facilitated in crystalline rocks by pressure release jointing which permits plucking by the ice.

Headwall sapping on this scale may account for the corrie headwall height without vertical overdeepening of the floor merely by the retreat of the face into the mountainside (Figure 71), yet where overdeepening is undoubtedly present it may be accounted for by rotational slip or extrusion flow (Figure 72).

Such proposals are by no means conclusive and research is continuing which may shed quite new light upon the origin of these spectacular features. Stand above Blea Water or at the lip of Small Water and try to visualise the ice collecting in the depression and the processes whereby a pre-glacial hollow, perhaps quite small, could become a deep amphitheatre.

The Small Water amphitheatre exhibits most of these classic features (Figure 70). The headwall is by no means vertical but has been greatly steepened and has eaten deeply into the upland mass. The sides curve round to create the 'armchair' shape, and the lower flanks are veneered with ablation moraine removed by mechanical action from the upper crags but never transported away from the hollow before the ice melted. The floor of the depression has been overdeepened in relation to the lip of cleaved tuffs (the lake level being determined by this lip) whose height was increased by the stage moraine. As the exit stream has cut through this drift to the solid rock so the lake level has fallen. During the more than 8,000 years of post-glacial time the basin has been steadily modified by screes loosened by mechanical processes from the crags and the delta deposits of streams tumbling down the steep flanks. Thus, the slopes left in a state of imbalance on the disappearance of the ice are being steadily brought into a state of balance.

The path traverses the screes and drift of the northern side and in the debris andesitic bedded tuffs can be examined around the bothie shelter, the well-spaced jointing producing regular large blocks and flags. These are water-lain materials, and in some of the blue-grey rocks the upward gradation from coarse to fine fragments can be followed. An individual gradation may be from a few inches to several feet thick and denotes the material emitted by one explosive eruption, the coarsest material falling first, ie forming the base of the bed, followed by successively finer material. In the crags above, several successive lava flows can be seen, standing as steps between the tuff beds, and a detailed examination suggests that the vents

of this volcano lay away to the west.

Along the stiff climb up the headwall to Nan Bield Pass, differential erosion has etched out examples of water-lain fine-bedded tuffs. Also during the climb, the view downvalley shows the feeder relationship of the Small Water ice to the main Haweswater valley.

At Nan Bield col the view reveals an excellent example of an incompletely developed corrie, the armchair shape being discernible but there is no overdeepening of the floor (Figure 73). Away to the south-west the craggy BVS changes abruptly to the lower, softer Silurian sedimentaries.

At this col one is standing at the crest of the anticline with dips beneath Harter Fell to the south

Fig 73: Partiallty Formed Corrie Above Kentmere

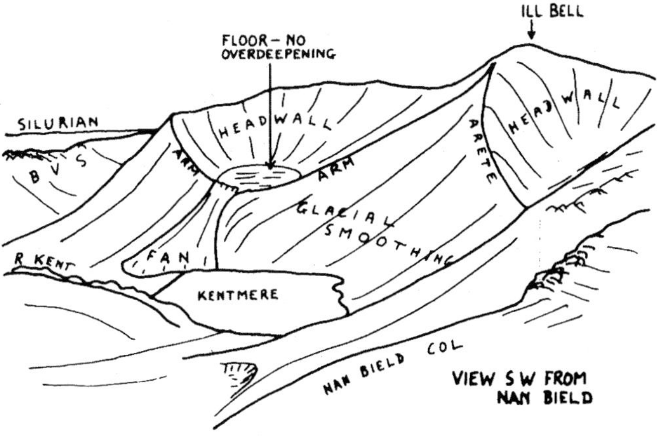

VIEW S W FROM NAN BIELD

and High Street to the north. It is possible to turn south across Harter Fell and thence to Mardale and the car park, but the northern loop on to High Street is the more rewarding. From the col the path climbs the convex slope on to High Street. After the scramble up the headwall this is an easy stroll to the trigonometrical point for here one is upon the roof of the Lake District, the highest erosion surface, often known as the 'High Street' surface and generally in excess of 2,300ft. From this summit on a clear day the whole of the Lake District is hid out with all the significant peaks identifiable. However, in the more immediate vicinity one can appreciate fully the impact of the Pleistocene glaciation upon the scenery, for the huge block of the High Street massif has been eaten away on all sides like a lump of cheese that has been bitten by numerous mice, leaving only the central boss intact. (Comparable features can be seen from the summit of Coniston Old Man.)

From High Street there is a lovely walk to Patterdale to the NW (398158), but the Haweswater loop is completed by walking east to the precipice of the Blea Water headwall (Figure 74). This is another perfect corrie, with headwall, tarn, morainic drift, lip, steep drop to the main valley

Fig 74: Glacial Features Around Blea Water

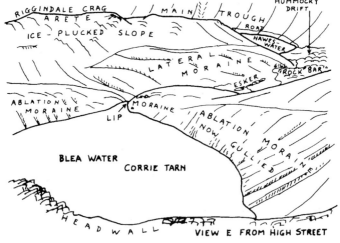

and an excellent arête, Riggindale Crag. A cairn marks the access point to the path down the arête (442112): this path while not as spectacular as the Striding Edge ridge walk on Helvellyn, does gives a direct impression of the shape of an arête. The ridge is broken by an ice-smoothed col across which ice once spilled, and in which a pond resembling a kettle hole sits (450112). From this col, traverse down to the lake and the heavy ablation moraine which fringes the hollow for 200ft or so above the lake can be seen to be deeply fretted by gullies. Exposures in these gullies reveal the angular and subangular debris in an earthy matrix, typically unsorted moraine detritus.

The lip has been artificially raised as the tarn now acts as a regulator within the Haweswater reservoir system but is heaped about with drift. Below the lip, the north flank of the valley is veneered by lobes of drift pointing diagonally downslope (Figure 74). This is lateral moraine whose lobate form has been caused by post-glacial streams and downslope wash. At first viewing they appear to be sub-ice fluvio-glacial features, but exposures in gullies along the path reveal the completely unsorted and unstratified nature of the debris-stones and pebbles in a brown earthy matrix.

In the floor of the valley are some small fluvio-glacial features, arguably eskers, now being dissected by a stream, the rounded profile and sinuous course being typical of such fluvio-glacial forms laid down in tunnels near a retreating ice-front. The valley is a series of rock steps, their downslope sides plucked and the upper sides smoothed and veneered. This would once have formed a crevassed ice-fall. Below the last rock step the fresh hummocky drift is seen clearly, while underfoot the whole walk from the tarn is littered with debris exhibiting all types of volcanic material from coarse andesitie agglomerates with fragments more than a foot across, through fine bedded tuffs showing excellent grading and evidence of their having been laid down subaqueously, to hard, black andesite lavas and pale rhyolites. The debris is generally angular and subangular, indicating its local origin and the great range of rock type found over a short horizontal and vertical distance in volcanic country. This results from the complex nature of a volcanic episode, with lava eruptions, explosions, gas clouds etc.

THE SHAP GRANITE INTRUSION AND ITS METAMORPHIC AUREOLE

Twelve miles north of Kendal beside the A6 (558084) are the

Fig 75: The Shap Granite Intrusion

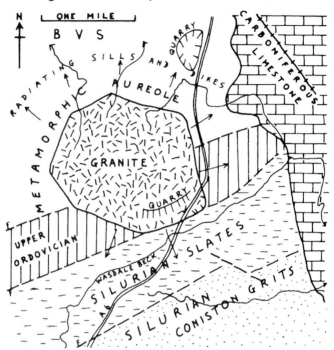

quarries of the Shap Granite Company marking the outcrop of the world-famous Shap Granite intrusion, a dome of approximately three square miles in area and roughly circular in shape (Figure 75). It is a plutonic igneous intrusion, ie it was injected into the existing country rock at great depth below the land surface, which resulted in the magma cooling very slowly thus enabling the mineral constituents to grow, produce well-formed crystals and a characteristically coarse-grained texture.

The intrusion is Devonian in age for it is intruded into and has metamorphosed the Silurian succession, while boulders of the granite are to be found in the Basal Conglomerate of the Lower Carboniferous which overlie these Silurian beds unconformably.

Like the other major intrusive masses of the Lake District, eg Skiddaw and Eskdale Granites, it was associated with the Caledonian mountain-building movements which brought to an end the Lower Palaeozoic cycle of sedimentation in the British area, causing many thousands of feet of deposits to be thrown into huge mountain chains with the characteristic NE-SW orientation.

As granitic intrusions are normally associated with mountain building, being injected into the roots of newly formed mountain systems, it is not surprising to find that structurally the Shap Granite lies at the heart of the mountains whose remnants compose today's Lake District. It is important to appreciate that the exposure of this deep-seated 'root material' is the result of the denudation to the point of virtual removal of those Caledonian mountains down some 350 million years of geological time from the Devonian to the present day.

While there is a consensus of agreement about the age of the granite, there is still debate concerning its mode of occurrence. Some consider it to be a cedar-tree laccolith, but the more popular view is that it is a stock or relatively small plug of material belonging to a much larger deeper mass (Figure 76).

Being a granite its chemical composition is acidic, ie its minerals are silica-rich and it contains a large proportion of quartz, although it is rather less acid than the Skiddaw and Eskdale Granites. These minerals are quartz, orthoclase felspar, plagioclase felspar, muscovite and biotite mica with a small percentage of hornblende. The feature which makes the Shap variety quite distinctive from other granites is the predominance of large well-formed, rectangular, pink orthoclase felspar crystals in a groundmass of smaller crystals of the other mineral constituents. It is these larger crystals which give the rock the texture known as

Fig 76: Possible Forms of the Shap Intrusion

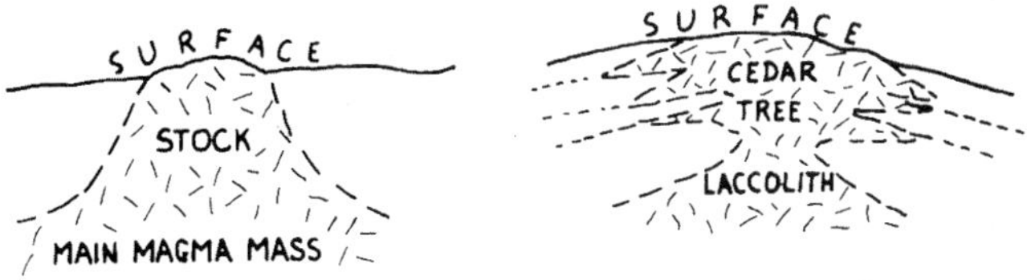

117

porphyritic, ie the predominance of large crystals of one mineral and the proportionately oversized minerals are called phenocrysts. Such a texture confirms the extremely slow cooling history of this magma. It is this distinctive texture and colour, along with the property of yielding to a high quality polish, which has made the Shap Granite so widely used as an ornamental stone.

An examination of the quarry itself reveals an interesting sequence of granite types and gives some indication of the stages through which the intrusion evolved. (Permission to visit this and the Bluestone quarry should be obtained from the manager at the main works south of Shap village - 568114.) There are three main varieties to be found: (a) on the flanks of the quarry is a light-coloured variety which contains a less-than-average percentage of the pink orthoclase felspars, although this is a less well-developed 'marginal' variety than is to be found in some other granites; (b) inside this is the main mass which has a distinct pink appearance, produced by these felspar crystals present in average quantity; (c) crossing this mass is a belt of very pink rock made up almost entirely of the porphyritic felspar.

These varieties are thought to represent three stages of injection from below, new and progressively felspar-rich material being drawn from a magma chamber as the intrusion forced its way upwards through the country rock. This proposition is supported by what could be considered a fourth phase, the injection of almost pure, finely crystalline orthoclase felspar known as aplite. This occurs as a series of dikes, which cut across all three main varieties, and occasionally possess a central quartz streak.

The dying stages of this activity are shown clearly by mineralisation as a result of gas action (pneumatolysis). Emanations of mineralised gases were forced through the fissure and joint systems, and have produced veins containing molybdenite, bismuthinite, pyrites, barytes and quartz which can be easily collected from the veins.

A crude system of vertical and horizontal joints caused by contraction of the magma on cooling gives the mass an impression of structure and results in the granite fracturing in massive rectangular blocks, a quality important in the quarrying operations. Towards the top and out to the sides of the mass this joint system is more compact and obvious, and also follows the line of the leading edge of the dome. At these extremities the magma naturally cooled more quickly, hence the much finer joints dividing the granite into a platy structure. Especially where a set of closely set vertical joints run from the surface above the intrusion, water has been able to percolate and through time has rotted the felspars, thereby breaking up the structure of the rock. Such zones are crumbly to the touch and have a distinctive green chloritic colour, chlorite being one of the alteration products resulting from chemical breakdown of felspars, eg at the western extremity of the quarry.

Another significant feature within the mass is the inclusion of patches of dark hard rock of little economic use and known to the miners as 'heathen'. Some are undoubtedly granitic and are thought to be the remnants of an initial phase of intrusion of a more basic material that was subsequently engulfed. Others are not granitic and analysis shows them to be pieces of the country rock through which the intrusion has passed, ie the intense upward pressure of the dome of magma through the existing rock caused them to crack, bend away and a large proportion of the roof material to fall into and be absorbed by the magma. Considering the temperatures involved and the speed at which this material would be melted and absorbed into the granite, the original pieces of roof material must have been quite massive for any to have survived before the final cooling of the mass.

The Shap Granite stock was forced into place approximately along the zone of junction between the Ordovician and the Silurian rock groups (Figure 75). As the metamorphic aureole is up to one mile wide it therefore affects a considerable range of rock types from the fissile Stockdale Shales to hard BVS ashes and lavas. Mineral changes are restricted to the first 1,300yd from the magmatic mass. Actual contacts can be seen in the slope north of the ruined Wasdale Head Farm (550082) where black, flinty, hornfelsed rocks abut against the pale granite.

The best locality for an examination of the effects of the metamorphism is the Bluestone Quarry cut into the northern sector of the aureole (564107). This large quarry is worked principally for road metal, the piles of dark-blue aggregate contrasting with the pink fragments of the crushed granite in the stockpile adjacent to the quarry. The rocks were originally andesites and andesitic ashes of the BVS and this quarry stands approximately 800 yards from the contact, the metamorphism being moderate.

The metamorphic effects fall into two categories, first the generalised local metamorphism of the country rock mass, and secondly the metasomatic changes along joint systems. A five-stage sequence has been worked out for the evolution of the aureole. First, the intrusion of the granite mass, which put considerable stress upon the country rocks. Second, the thermal metamorphism, which hardened the rocks and increased the silica and potassium content. Third, the first stage of the metasomatic processes, which included the formation of epidote and garnet along fissures by the emanation of mineralised fluids and gases from the magma under pressure, containing, for example, silica and calcium. As the emanating materials cooled, there followed a crystallisation sequence dependent upon the chemical constituents and their crystallisation temperatures.

The most common results of this activity are veins with a mid green epidote outer zone and a deep-red garnetiferous inner zone which may well be shattered and itself veined with quartz and calcite. Nonetheless, well-formed garnet crystals are to be found.

The fourth stage saw the development of sericite from the felspars and biotite in the hornfelsed (ie metamorphosed) andesites of the country rock, especially around veins containing pyrites (the shining 'fool's gold'). Once more the gases being forced through the fissures caused the changes, although this time the metamorphism is within the country rocks themselves in a zone up to 10ft on either side of the fissure. The fifth and final stage involved mineralisation as a result of hydrothermal action, the hot water indicating much lower temperatures than in the earlier phases. The principal minerals produced, seen along veins and joints, were molybdenite, bright shining blue, the glistening pyrites and dark bismuthinite. Immediately north of Bluestone Quarry are the main works of the Shap Granite Company where granite not used for ornamental work and the bluestone are used for the making of kerbstones and wide-diameter pipes seen stacked in the yards.

Chapter 7

Buttermere–Crummock and Ennerdale

THESE TWO glacial troughs radiate north-westwards from the BVS crags of Great Gable-Brandreth (211103), crossing the Ennerdale Granophyre outcrop and the Skiddaw Slates of the Buttermere, Loweswater and Ennerdale Fells (Figure 77). There is no through road along Ennerdale, cars being prohibited beyond the forestry gate above Bowness Knott (113155). This, with the rugged mountains at its head, and the extensive afforestation, makes Ennerdale one of the loneliest and emptiest major valleys of the Lake District. In contrast the Buttermere-Crummock Water trough is on one of the most heavily followed scenic routes of the National Park, which loops from Keswick via the B5289, up Borrowdale, over Honister Pass to Cockermouth and thence past Bassenthwaite to Keswick once more. At the head of each valley a network of paths criss-cross the rolling upper surfaces of Fleetwith, dispersing over this central mountain knot of the Lake District.

BUTTERMERE-CRUMMOCK WATER

The classic view of this valley is from Fleetwith Pike (206142), which is approached by a long climb from Gatesgarth (196150), or from the

Honister Slate works at the summit of Honister Pass (225135). The fell slopes above the pass are spattered with disused and active slate workings which lie at the western end of the highly cleaved zone of Bedded Tuffs of the BVS which extend ENE into Borrowdale. The workings are often tunnels, but today, high up the fells, open scars are being worked. The quarries have operated continuously from the mid-seventeenth century, producing the famous grey-green slates from a 300ft band of the Middle Tuffs. These tuffs are typical of the Bedded Tuffs, which have produced the regular persistent cleavage necessary for economic slate working. In origin they were deposits of fine particles worked out from existing volcanic material and redeposited subaqueously, hence the clear bedding. Later compression produced the cleavage, and as with the Elterwater slates and the Coniston slates this is set at a high angle to the bedding. The cleavage is well seen if the old tram track is followed above the Honister Slate works and then the path to Fleetwith Pike. Both in the currently worked faces, and in the weathered outcrops beside the path, excellent examples occur of

Fig 77: Generalised Geology of Buttermere-Crummock-Ennerdale

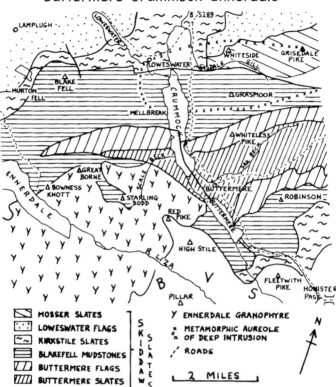

MOSSER SLATES
LOWESWATER FLAGS
KIRKSTILE SLATES
BLAKEFELL MUDSTONES
BUTTERMERE FLAGS
BUTTERMERE SLATES

SKIDDAW SLATES

Y ENNERDALE GRANOPHYRE
METAMORPHIC AUREOLE OF DEEP INTRUSION
ROADS

2 MILES

N

the near-vertical cleavage planes contrasting with the gender southerly dip of the beds. This S to SSE dip is caused by the location on the northern limb of the great Scafell syncline which runs WSW-ENE through the Scafell Range, or alternatively, on the southern limb of the Skiddaw anticline.

From Fleetwith Pike the full beauty of the Buttermere trough can be appreciated (Figure 78). Below the Middle Tuffs of the summit lie the Lower Andesites which themselves lie unconformably upon the Skiddaw Slates across the snout of the fell. Except for a small area of granophyre at the north-western corner of Buttermere, the valley floor is underlain by the Blakefell mudstones of the Skiddaw Slates. We are here at the northern limit of the main BVS outcrop which extends along the upper flanks of Burtness Comb to High Stile (171148). The whole of the north-eastern flank of the valley is composed of Skiddaw Slates, while on the south-western flank the BVS are succeeded by the belt of Ennerdale Granophyre stretching from Red Pike (161155) across Ennerdale to Ennerdale Forest. By the time Crummock Water is reached, the country on all sides is unmistakably of Skiddaw Slate.

The trough is fault-guided and exhibits features of glacial overdeepening with a marked break of slope at a shoulder delimiting the extent of this gouging. Above the shoulder, side valleys are left hanging. There are, however, important contrasts between the two flanks. The north-eastern flank, ie that facing SW, is smoothed, except for the gash of Sail Beck, whereas the SW face is fretted by a series of fine corries (Figure 79). These corrie-hollows, Burtness Comb, Bleaberry Tarn Comb and Ling Comb, are scalloped into the face above the shoulder with

Fig 78: The Buttermere - Crummock Trough

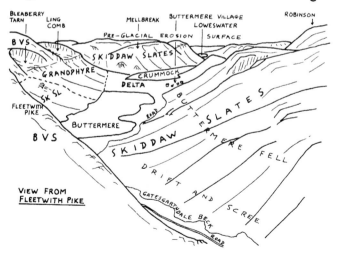

Fig 79: The Three Buttermere Corries from Fleetwith Pike

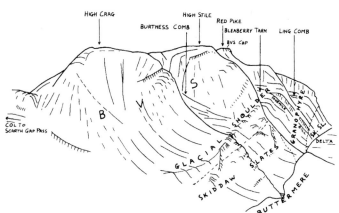

little regard for the changing rock type or structure, eg they are cut across all three of the rock groups. The significant factor is their north-easterly orientation which gave maximum shade and hence maximum névé accumulation. This NE orientation is the most common direction for the Lake District corries in general.

The view from Fleetwith Pike extends in a westward and southward sweep over the BVS country from the ice-worked col of Scarth Gap Pass (189135), separating the buttresses and knobs of High Crag and the Haystacks, which hide Ennerdale. Beyond rises the dark mass of Pillar and the line of mountains

leading to Great Gable (211103), a line broken by the flat col of Black Sail Pass (191114). To the north-east stretch the Skiddaw Slate ribs of the Derwent Fells which drop down to Borrowdale, while Skiddaw itself peeps out beyond the Derwent basin. Such viewpoints enable us to envisage the ice-tongues spilling outwards from the central hill mass, and with the aid of their embedded load, gouging out the U-shaped troughs of the present landscape.

Three further features in the evolution of the trough are worthy of note. First, the very deep incision of the valley has been assisted by the presence of a fault along its length, which persists as a shatter belt through the upper valley towards Honister. Second, the extent of the overdeepening below the valley shoulder: the steep sides and the abrupt trough end at Gatesgarth all illustrate the principle that the valley glaciers concentrated their destructive energy downwards and not laterally. This contrasts with the much shallower Coniston valley where the ice-stream divided and thus diffused its energies. Third, the Buttermere delta, which separates the two lakes, is often quoted as an example of the power of a stream to obtain, transport and deposit material. There is no doubt that the post-glacial Sail Beck, with its steep longitudinal gradient, has incised deeply into the Skiddaw Slates and has produced a considerable alluvial and gravel fan to create the division of the two lakes. However, the rock floor of the trough is, at this location, only a few feet below present lake level, although in both directions the floor is much deeper (Figure 80). This is a classic example of a rock bar, possibly associated with metamorphic hardening near the Ennerdale Granophyre contact, which has resisted the power of the ice and its abrasive load. Thus, the waters of Sail Beck, spilling into the still and here shallow waters of the lake, were able to build up their sediments rapidly, causing the separation of the lakes. The separation was aided further by the gradual fall of the lake level as the exit stream from Crummock Water lowered its overflow. The Derwentwater-Bassenthwaite division is an even larger example and both the deltas have been created within the past 15,000 years.

The upper valley of Gatesgarthdale exhibits some fine screes from the Middle Tuffs of the BVS, which give way to the smoother flanks of Blakefell Mudstones and Kirkstile Slates, or the Skiddaw Slate series,

Fig 80: Simplified Long Profile

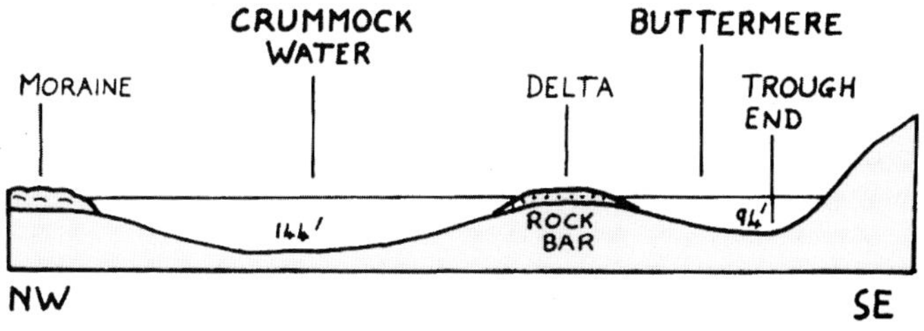

although the junctions are obscured by screes, solifluction and gravity deposits and lateral moraines. Some of the debris near the upper bridge (210150) is of huge BVS blocks of tuffs up to 15ft in diameter from Honister Crag. The first Skiddaw beds observable below the BVS are the dark blue-black Kirkstile Slates with their distinctive striping, which is particularly prominent in water-washed specimens in Gatesgarthdale Beck. Above Gatesgarth itself fawn to grey mudstones and siltstones of the Blakefell Mudstones come in, to continue in a broad sweep across Robinson (201169) and along the western flank of Buttermere. At Gatesgarth the trough broadens suddenly and the extensive alluvial infilling at the head of Buttermere is evident in the flat watermeadows.

WALK FROM BUTTERMERE VILLAGE

Buttermere village is perched on a cluster of Skiddaw Slate rock-knobs, which are both ice-smoothed and scratched and partially plastered by drift. The very dark blue slates show high-angle cleavage and contorted bedding, but owe their hardness and hence their survival to the proximity of the Ennerdale Granophyre, eg exposures at the church, the Mountain Rescue Post (177170) and the car park in the small quarry below the village.

Immediately below the ancient cluster of farms – now also hotels and cafes – the gentle slope of the Sail Beck delta begins, and its scale can be appreciated, approximately three quarters of a mile long and more than a quarter of a mile wide. Cross this fertile delta and take the upper of the two footbridges (172164). At the stream the change of rock type is first evident, for the bed is composed largely of pink rubble, which denotes the passage onto the Ennerdale Granophyre outcrop, here at its most easterly point. Strike upslope, following the cairned footpath through the conifers. Beyond this plantation the steep climb emphasises the extent of the overdeepening by the main valley-glacier. The pink debris continues until the lip of the corrie or cwm hollow. This lip is a large, arcuate morainic mass, including some very large blocks, and was formed as the ice-front retreated finally into its hollow. This corrie 'hangs' above the main trough and Sourmilk Gill has cut deeply into the moraine as it cascades over the lip.

From the moraine the fine headwall can be seen, with the vertical cliffs of Chapel Crags composed of the Lower Andesites of the BVS, and several thick lava flows can be picked out, each exhibiting flow-brecciation in their upper sections. Ascending diagonally towards Red Pike (on the right of the view), these andesites are cut out by the underlying Skiddaw Slates, the junction being a thrust plane similar to that at Ullswater (Chapter 4). The junction is difficult to examine because of the screes.

The lower flanks of the hollow are heavily masked in drift from the melting in situ of the lingering ice-mass. The path ascends The Saddle, the red rocks indicating the continuance here of the granophyre, although it begins to show marginal characteristics, eg finer texture. The capping of Red Pike is controversial: it seems to be of BVS,

here dark flinty rocks hardened by thermal metamorphism. A thin sliver of Skiddaw Slate, also baked and flinty, appears to lie beneath, forming the actual roof rock of the intrusion, although mapping is made extremely difficult by the frost-shattering which has littered the summit area with rubble.

Red Pike provides a viewpoint from which to appreciate the granophyre scenery, for in the foreground to the north-west lies Gale Fell, followed westwards beyond Ennerdale valley by the rolling surfaces of Ennerdale Forest (Figure 81). The scenery is remarkably similar to that developed on the Eskdale Granite-smoothed rolling country, with

Fig 81: Lower Ennerdale from Red Pike

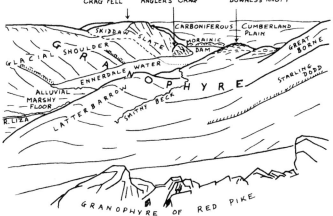

few strong crags – in stark contrast to the crags of Pillar mountain in upper Ennerdale which takes us back to the BVS, and contrasting, too, with the more conical appearance of the Skiddaw Slates to the north. Crags are found, however, on some northerly slopes where the well-developed jointing system has assisted the frost action, which followed the ice-plucking at maximum glaciation, eg Iron Crag (126122).

The Ennerdale Granophyre is the second largest of the Lake District intrusions and regarded as a one-stage stock in general form with flat roof and steep sides (Figure 82) intruded in the Devonian period. This form is indicated by the junction seen in the field, eg the sides of the stock are exposed in the junction running upslope from Buttermere and the flat roof illustrated by the low-angle junctions across Red Pike or Crag Fell south of Ennerdale Water (100143).

The granophyre is a pink to pink-brown rock, fine to medium in grain,

non-porphyritic and dominated by felspar and quartz, with the less abundant ferromagnesian minerals usually chloritised and identifiable as ill-defined greenish blotches. In addition to this normal granophyre, two deviant types are found: first, a marginal granophyre, usually fine-grained but with prominent felspar crystals giving a porphyritic appearance; and second, a set of dark, more basic rocks, usually dolerite. This dolerite seems to have been injected immediately prior to the main granophyre intrusion and the variations in the basic rock types found are reflections of the different stages of absorption achieved by the granophyre before cooling and solidification.

The fact that although the granophyre stock has been injected along the Skiddaw Slate-BVS junction, it is the result of replacement and assimilation of pre-existing rocks rather than forced emplacement involving displacement is implied by the lack of arching in the surrounding rocks

Fig 82: Form of the Ennerdale Stock

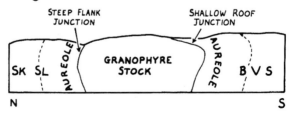

Fig 83: Structures of the Skiddaw Slates

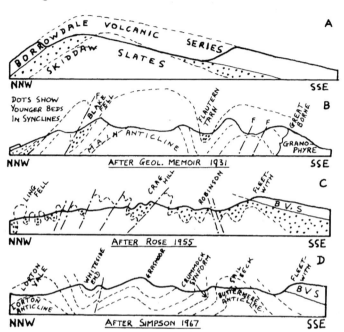

A

BORROWDALE VOLCANIC SERIES
SKIDDAW SLATES

NNW   SSE

B

DOTS SHOW YOUNGER BEDS IN SYNCLINES

FEW BLAKE FELL   FLAUTERN TARN   GREAT BORNE

MAIN ANTICLINE   F F   GRANO-PHYRE

NNW   AFTER GEOL. MEMOIR 1931   SSE

C

LING FELL   CRAG HILL   ROBINSON   FLEET WITH   B.V.S

NNW   AFTER ROSE 1955   SSE

D

LORTON VALE   WHITESIDE END   GRASMOOR   CRUMMOCK SYNFORM   SAIL BECK   FLEET-WITH   B V S

LORTON ANTICLINE   BUTTERMERE ANTICLINE

NNW   AFTER SIMPSON 1967   SSE

and the absence of much of the lowest Skiddaw Slate beds against which the granophyre lies.

The granophyre has a well-developed jointing system, which assists the fragmentation of the mass. Thus, not only are Ennerdale Granophyre glacial erratics plentiful along the western sides of England and Wales, but today the upper surfaces are littered with debris as the result of frost action, eg the upper sections of Red Pike.

Directly north-west from Red Pike lie the rounded granophyre hills of Gale Fell and Great Borne (Figure 106) but beyond, in a sweeping arc away to the north-east, lie the Skiddaw Slate hills. This principal outcrop of the Skiddaw Slates provides an excellent example of the changing understanding and interpretation of an area. In essence, this northern section of the Lake District is an asymmetrical anticline with a

Fig 84: Structural Lines in the Skiddaw Slates

After Rose and Simpson

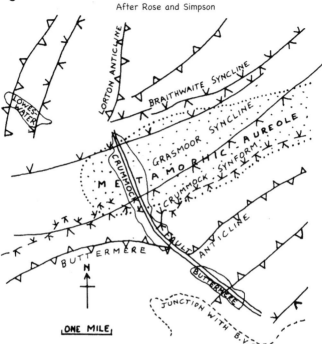

steeper northern limb and an ENE-WSW trend, breached to expose the older Skiddaw Slates and leaving the overlying BVS as inward-facing fringes (Figure 83).

The next level of complexity lies in the recognition of an anticlinorium structure for the slates (Figure 83). The intense folding of these latter rocks in comparison with the simple flexures of the BVS has been accounted for by the greater competence of the volcanic materials, which are deformed more by thrusting and faulting. It became orthodox thinking (Geological Memoir, 1931) to categorise the whole of the Skiddaw Slates into two major groups: a lower arenaceous series of flags, sandstones and grits, known as the Loweswater Flags, and an upper argillaceous series of mudstones, siltstones and shales known as the Mosser-Kirkstile Slates. The complex repetition of the beds was seen as the result of the sharp folds, the younger slates being preserved in the synclines (Figure 83B and C).

In 1967 a paper by Simpson was published (Figure 83D) which suggested that the Skiddaw Slates should be thought of as a series of alternating arenaceous and argillaceous sediments giving a total of eight subdivisions:

TABLE 5 Skiddaw Slate Succession (after Simpson 1967)

> Sunderland Slates
> Watch Hill Grits and Flags
> Mosser Slates
> Loweswater Flags
> Kirkstile Slates
> Blakefell Mudstones
> Buttermere Flags
> Buttermere Slates

Furthermore, a period of orogenic activity within the Ordovician period produced three identifiable fold and fault phases, all with a general ENE-WSW trend (Figure 84). According to Simpson, the complex outcrops and dip variations seen today are the result of the interaction of these three phases, part of what is known as the pre-Bala orogeny, and pre-date the deposition of the BVS, before which event prolonged erosion and denudation of the Skiddaw Slates took place. This produced the marked angular unconformity claimed by Simpson which runs contrary to the findings of workers in other localities, including some mentioned in this book, who have suggested a conformable Skiddaw Slate-BVS junction, eg by the intercalation of lava flows with the argillaceous beds. The Caledonian orogeny of the Devonian period, which created the major Skiddaw anticline, lifted both the Skiddaw Slates and the BVS into the asymmetrical arch but left intact the pre-existing structures in the former series.

Most recently (1972) Moseley has proposed that although there is an unconformity between the Skiddaw Slates and the BVS, the pre-Bala folding was not severe. The contrast in tectonic style between the two is the result of their differing competence, the major orogenic activity being Caledonian, ie post-BVS.

A further complication may be added by the introduction of the Ennerdale Granophyre and another, unexposed mass, possibly linked to the Skiddaw Granite, underlying Grasmoor (Figure 77). These intrusions have yielded metamorphic aureoles up to two miles wide, with varying degrees

Fig 85: Upper Buttermere from Red Pike

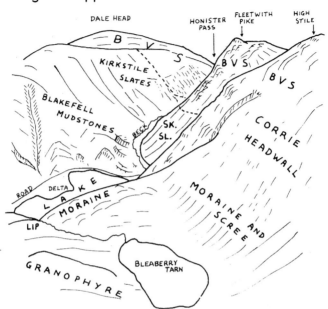

of hardening and baking, eg the dark flinty debris at the summit of Red Pike.

It is upon these tectonic variables that the physical agencies of landform formation have acted to produce the current landscape. West of Crummock Water the breached Buttermere Anticline (Figure 84) exposes the oldest beds, the Buttermere Slates and Flags in a belt from the lake shore east of Scale Knott (153177) to Flautern Tarn (125171). The very dark-blue, fine-grained, striped slates, easily confused with the Kirkstile and Mosser Slates, are distinguishable from the much paler, grey to fawn, coarser flags seen immediately north of Scale Beck. To the north, the steep dips of the wide exposures of the dark fine-grained Blake Fell Mudstones across Blake Fell (111197) to Mellbreak (143195) are the result of the exposure of the upper limb of the Crummock synform. This synform accentuated the pre-existing anticline and the whole belt is within the metamorphic aureole. It has taken prolonged and severe denudation to reduce the structures to the rounded stumps seen today.

Across the Buttermere trough to the north-east the scenery developed around Grasmoor (176203) is among the strongest anywhere on the Skiddaw Slate outcrop. Extensive screes and some crags break up the usual smoothness of outline although the pre-glacial erosion surfaces have survived in places, eg Grasmoor summit. East from Whiteside End (170220) runs the sharp Braithwaite syncline whose southern limb produces the crags of Mosser Slates and Loweswater Flags of Gasdale Crags and Grisedale Pike (198227).

Grasmoor lies at the heart of the main arch of the region with dips to north and south, while the southern flanks are affected by the Crummock synform. Furthermore, this area with its deeply incised valleys and extensive screes is within the metamorphosed zone of hardened rocks, which extends from Loweswater to Barrow (228219). The Crummock synform runs across Whiteless Pike, giving near-vertical bedding along the north flank of Sail Beck valley. Immediately to the south, from Buttermere village, along lower Sail Beck and over Knott Rigg, runs the axis of the Buttermere anticline which exposes the lowest Skiddaw Slate Beds, the Buttermere Slates and Flags. The combination of the synform and the anticline produces the complex pattern of dips, often steep, seen in Buttermere village, eg the rock-knob on which the church stands, and on either side of the road to Newlands. (NB Take care to distinguish between dip and cleavage orientation.)

From Red Pike summit it is possible to continue into Ennerdale over areas described later in this chapter, or to return to Buttermere. This return journey yields a fine view of the Bleaberry Tarn hollow with its morainic dam (Figure 85), and on to the upper trough of Buttermere along the Gatesgarthdale shatter belt. The topography of this upper section gives very little indication of rock change along the flanks, which are everywhere concave and extensively buried in drift and scree. Above these flanks lie the remnant pre-glacial erosion surfaces.

A second walk from Buttermere village leads across the delta and over the lovely Scale Force Bridge (169166). This is a much easier walk than the first route, albeit distinctly wet underfoot, and affords fine views of the main valley. Beyond the bridge the dark-blue, cleaved Buttermere Slates appear in the path and from this point there are recurrent outcrops and rubble. Interspersed with this dark material, especially where gills cross the path, is the bright red debris which indicates the presence of the granophyre immediately upslope across the flanks of Scales. This granophyre is usually of the marginal porphyritic type.

The lower flanks are plastered with boulder clays, sometimes exposed as red or yellow heavy clays and elsewhere indicated by extremely boggy country. These seem to be part of extensive dumps of lateral moraine over which scree is creeping (Figure 86).

The path towards Scale Force provides good views of the truncated spurs of Mellbreak above Crummock Water (Figure 87) – the Scale Beck delta creeping forward into the lake, the moraines damming the outlet, the waters fully covering the valley floor. In addition, the site of Buttermere village and the delta form can be appreciated, including the Skiddaw Slate rock-knobs.

The granophyre/slate junction is masked, but the dark Buttermere Slates can be seen along the path through the col into Mosedale (148173) and along the flanks of Scale Knott where the dark fragmented screes contrast with the light, blocky granophyre screes across Scales (155170).

ENNERDALE

Approached from the north via Lamplugh (089209), Ennerdale remains hidden until one rounds

Fig 86: Slope Facets Along Scale Force Path

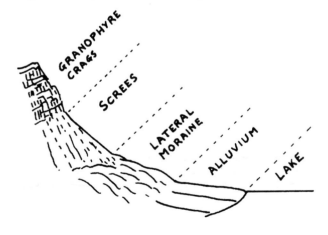

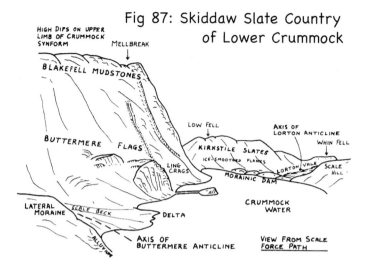

Fig 87: Skiddaw Slate Country of Lower Crummock

HIGH DIPS ON UPPER LIMB OF CRUMMOCK SYNFORM

MELLBREAK

BLAKEFELL MUDSTONES

BUTTERMERE FLAGS

LING CRAGS

LOW FELL

KIRKSTILE SLATES

ICE-SMOOTHED FLANKS

AXIS OF LORTON ANTICLINE

WHIN FELL

LORTON VALE

SCALE HILL

MORAINIC DAM

CRUMMOCK WATER

LATERAL MORAINE

SCALE BECK

DELTA

ALLUVIUM

AXIS OF BUTTERMERE ANTICLINE

VIEW FROM SCALE FORCE PATH

the shoulder of Murton Fell when it opens out, shielded by its twin buttresses of Bowness Knott and Angler's Crag (Figure 88). The lane from Lamplugh runs across smooth rolling Skiddaw Slate country, mostly Blakefell Mudstones pinched into the Crummock synform.

Superimposed upon this solid geology are a variety of glacial and fluvio-glacial features. As in the Eskdale district to the south (Chapter 8), the classical interpretation of the late glacial period in lower Ennerdale and its effects on the scenery has been to propose a progressive separation of

Fig 88: View up Ennerdale - SE from Croasland

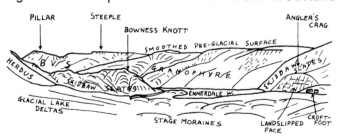

PILLAR

STEEPLE

BOWNESS KNOTT

ANGLER'S CRAG

SMOOTHED PRE-GLACIAL SURFACE

HERDUS

SKIDDAW SLATES

GRANOPHYRE

SKIDDAW SLATES

ENNERDALE W.

GLACIAL LAKE DELTAS

STAGE MORAINES

LANDSLIPPED FACE

CROFT-FOOT

Fig 89: Glacial Features of Lower Ennerdale
(after Huddart)

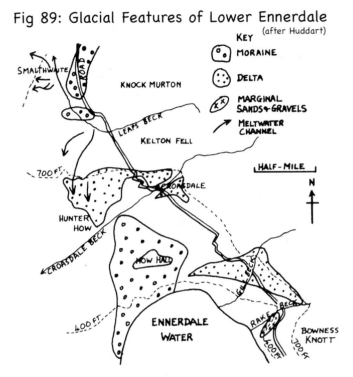

KEY

MORAINE

DELTA

MARGINAL SANDS & GRAVELS

MELTWATER CHANNEL

SMALTHWAITE

KNOCK MURTON

LEAPS BECK

KELTON FELL

~700 FT

CROASDALE

HUNTER HOW

CROASDALE BECK

HOW HALL

ENNERDALE WATER

~400 FT

BOWNESS KNOTT

RAKE

400 FT

700 FT

HALF-MILE

N

the two main ice-masses, the Lake District and Irish Sea ice-sheets. The westward retreat of the Irish Sea ice-front produced a series of successively lower pro-glacial lakes from 800ft and 400ft OD ponded between the ice and the hills to the east. Sediment from streams pouring into these lakes yielded a sequence of deltas accordant with the lake levels. The exit streams from the lakes were said to have cut a sequence of successively lower ice-margin meltwater channels, eg the Nannycatch gorge.

There are, indeed, deposits of delta gravels (Figure 89) and there was an ice-marginal lake which existed at several levels, but it seems probable that much of the water was carried away along englacial and subglacial channels and that the level of the lakes and hence the deltas was determined by the englacial water table. Many of the meltwater channels are now regarded as sub-glacial in origin.

From Lamplugh, in an arc to Bowness Knott (112155), several such deltas have been placed on to the shoulder of the fells between 800ft and 400ft OD. The most prominent are those athwart Croasdale Beck and Gill Beck, and are crossed by the lane to Ennerdale. They are typically flat-topped, with steep frontal slopes, generally lobate in plan and occasionally kettle-holed on their upper surface. Other deposits, such as that on which Bowness Cottage stands (108155), seem to be gravel benches formed marginal to the ice.

The spoil-heaps and trackways seen along Kelton Fell (095181) are the remains of extensive haematite mining, worked from veins up to 20ft wide in the Skiddaw Slate, particularly during World War One.

Ennerdale Water reflects in its shape the tongue of ice at a specific retreat stage. As far downvalley as Angler's Crag (100150) the trough and ice-lobe remained constricted, but suddenly the ice was able to spill into a wider basin. Once it broadened in this fashion it lost much of its downward erosive power and the marked overdeepening ceased, eg the waters are 150ft deep above Angler's Crag but the lower portions are shallower. Much of the ice in this lower basin seems to have stagnated and melted in situ, for there is a complex area of gravel patches and clays from lakelets etc around the lake below 400ft. However, the extensive morainic mounds around How Hall (090164) which block off much of the valley are not, in the main, stage moraines from the Ennerdale glacier, but result mostly from a readvance of the Irish Sea ice which may even have overridden some Lake District ice before melting in situ. Evidence for this origin is found in the presence of Carboniferous and Triassic St Bees materials in this moraine, ie materials found only to the west.

The craggy knob of Bowness Knott is one of the best locations for the examination of the junction of the granophyre with the Skiddaw Slate. The western half of the hill is of Skiddaw Slate and the eastern half of Ennerdale Granophyre, and this near-vertical junction is along the flanks of the stock. The Skiddaw Slates, well seen in the roadstone quarry near the car park, are much hardened almost to quartzites by contact metamorphism and quite unrecognisable as Blakefell Mudstone, although the bedding is sometimes identifiable. The shortest route to the summit is up the sharp screes of the western face, but a less strenuous and equally rewarding path leaves the lane near Rake Beck

(110160) and skirts the plantation to the fault-guided col separating the Knott from Great Borne. Along this path there are many examples of the baking of the Skiddaw Slates and of the injection of granophyre veins and tongues into the country rock. In addition, felsitic dikes occur, distinguishable by their pale coloration and pink felspar crystals, eg where the path squeezes past the forestry fence.

Along the summit crags the actual slate-granophyre junction is observable, with marked slate hardening and cleavage. Despite the afforestation, immediately east of the summit a mass of black dolerite is observable. This is a fragment of the basic intrusion, which seems to have been injected immediately before the granophyre

and partially assimilated by it. Veins of the acid rock criss-cross the fine-grained dolerite.

The col between Bowness Knott and Great Borne is partially filled by moraines left by the ice passing through the depression. The junction is evident again on Herdus (118162) where if the slope is followed towards Great Borne, the steep dips of the Skiddaw Slates give way to the blocky, rounded pink granophyres just east of a marked gully. The slope of Great Borne is crossed diagonally by the pale outcrop of a rhyolite dike, containing lovely pink spherulites.

The sequence along each flank of Ennerdale can be followed conveniently from Bowness Knott by the use of the two sections in Figure 90. Along the northern

Fig 90: Simplified Sections Along Ennerdale Flanks

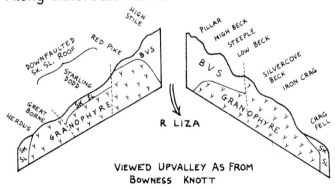

VIEWED UPVALLEY AS FROM BOWNESS KNOTT

flank the Herdus Skiddaw Slates are replaced by the granophyre of Great Borne. Next, a portion of the Skiddaw Slate roof to the stock has been down-faulted on to Starling Dodd (142158) where the olive and grey Blakefell Mudstones are readily identifiable in the few outcrops. The granophyres reappear around Red Pike with its BVS capping, and from High Stile (170148) the true BVS topography asserts itself.

The southern flank of Ennerdale possesses some interesting features, the first of which is Angler's Crag, directly across from Bowness Knott. This is a spur truncated by ice, but has suffered further from the overdeepening of the trough which has made its front face unstable. There have been several landslips which account for the stepped broken front to the crag. Like Bowness Knott, it is composed of hardened Blakefell Mudstones and immediately east of the crag the granophyre junction climbs vertically towards Crag Fell (099145) before the roof is reached and a low-angle junction curves round the shoulder of the fell.

The second feature is the dark mass or 'raft' of dolerite which runs along the crags for a mile upvalley from Crag Fell. This mass, more than 250ft thick in places and identifiable by the dark

crags, is similar in character to the Bowness Knott dolerite. The broad shoulder of Steeple (157117), built of granophyre, is capped by the crags which denote the coming of the BVS, and the impressive sweep of mountains from Pillar to Green Gable (215108) are built upon the thousands of feet of Lower Andesites with occasional tuffs and dacites which dip generally away from the viewpoint to the SSE.

The north-facing flank is scalloped by corrie-hollows which 'hang' above the shoulder of overdeepening, causing some fine cascading streams. This contrasts with the smoothness of the south-facing wall. The alignment of this valley is fault-guided and the River Liza is a misfit. Nonetheless, the floor is marshy for some way above the lake, where considerable alluvial deposition is steadily shortening the lake. Despite the deposition and aggradation of parts of the valley floor, the granophyre-BVS junction is seen in the stream close to the footbridge above High Beck (160138) where the red granophyre abuts against the hardened brittle Lower Andesites. In the valley floor around Black Sail Youth Hostel (140140) there are patches of hummocky drift where ice of the last 'mini-glaciation' melted in situ, perhaps only some 9,000 years BP.

Chapter 8

Eskdale

THE LOVELY VALLEY of the River Esk owes its attraction largely to the variety of the scenery it offers. The waters collect in the upland basin immediately below the eastern flanks of the Scafell Pikes (216072), pass through fine gorges, along a glacial valley, and meander to the sea across a broad estuary beyond Ravenglass (085963).

The scenery is dominated by two groups of rocks (Figure 91): the BVS and the igneous intrusion of Eskdale Granite. In addition, the glaciers and their meltwaters worked hard on these rocks to produce contrasting topography. The result of the geological and geomorphological interactions is a valley which can be divided into five distinct topographic sections: first, the upper basin above Throstle Garth (228038); second, from the Garth to Wha House bridge (204009); third, a middle section to Eskdale Green (142002); fourth, a lower stretch from Eskdale Green to the A595 bridge (112964); and fifth, the estuary.

Unlike many lakeland valleys, there is no straightforward road or track following the full length of the valley. Furthermore, the broken nature of some sections and the patchy woodland make it difficult to obtain clear impressions of the valley form from the floor. Nonetheless, surfaced roads do follow much of the valley and provide access to viewpoints. The A595 Whitehaven road angles its way around the western end of Muncaster Fell and across the lower floodplain, but access to the middle valley is via Miterdale to Eskdale Green. From this point the road winds along the best-known parts of the valley until it branches beyond Wha House bridge for the strenuous wriggle over the Hard Knott Pass to the upper Duddon basin. Upper Eskdale is attainable by an easy path to the Lingcove Beck junction at Throstle Garth, followed by an energetic ascent to the uppermost basin, which then gives access by a well-worn path to Scafell summit.

As a change from many of the traverses in this book, Eskdale is dealt with from the upper reaches downwards. The best viewpoint from which to appreciate the layout of the area is the summit of Hard Knott Pass (232019). From the road the upper valley above Brotherilkeld (212014) cannot be seen, but a warming scramble from the road to the summit of Hard Knott and Border End (228019) is rewarded by a panoramic sweep over the Esk basin and much

Fig 91: Solid Geology of Eskdale

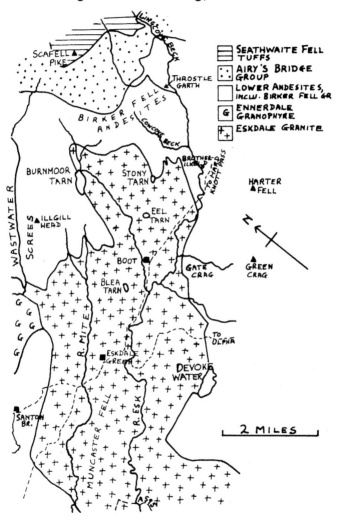

Legend:
- SEATHWAITE FELL TUFFS
- AIRY'S BRIDGE GROUP
- LOWER ANDESITES, INCLU. BIRKER FELL GR
- G ENNERDALE GRANOPHYRE
- ESKDALE GRANITE

2 MILES

of central lakeland, including spectacular views of Scafell and upper Great Langdale (Figure 92).

The upper basin sits on the southern limb of the great Scafell synclinorium which runs through the Scafell range with an ENE-WSW trend, giving a general northerly dip to the rocks of upper Eskdale and the visible flanks of the Scafell range (see also Chapter 5). However, the fact that this is a synclinorium and not a simple syncline is illustrated by a minor anticlinal axis which runs along Eskdale above Brotherilkeld to Throstle Garth, giving south-easterly dips on Yew Crags (221020) and Border End.

The splendid BVS scenery seen stretching away northwards from Border End is carved into the thick, predominantly andesitic lavas and tuffs of the Lower Andesites, the Airy's Bridge Group which includes most of the more acid members, and the Seathwaite Fell Tuffs of the upper Scafell Crags (Figure 92). The gorge sections of the Esk and Lingcove Beck dropping to Throstle Garth are cut into thick lavas within the Birker Fell Andesites where the northerly dip is clearly shown and the waters are cascading down the scarp slope. Below Throstle Garth the valley assumes a more classic U-shape, with well-marked glacial shoulder at the top of Yew Crags, denoting the extent of overdeepening produced by the valley-glacier. The upper basin provided an excellent

Fig 92: Upper Esk Basin from Hard Knott

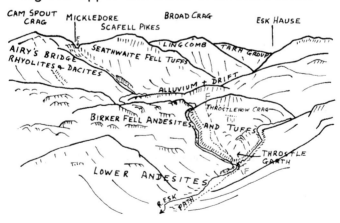

collecting ground for this glacier, while at least during the higher ice levels additional supplies spilled over the Hard Knott col from upper Duddondale, eg striations and polished rocks in the pass.

Still from Border End the middle section of Eskdale can be seen to Eskdale Green, with considerable woodland including remnants of the once-extensive oak woods and a system of stone walls showing the limits of man's improvements. These improvements are now being pushed back by the downslope encroachment of bracken, which threatens to engulf the upper walls and intakes. On the ledge of Yew Crags sits the beautifully symmetrical Roman fort of Mediobogdum (219015). The ledges represent the tops of lava-flows, usually over 100ft thick, and are indicated in the road whose gradient is a series of alternating flattish sections and steep twists.

Middle Eskdale consists of broad flat stretches and more constricted broken sections. Below Wha House bridge (204009) the valley floor, north flank and lower sections of the south flank are underlain by the Eskdale Granite. This granite produces generally subdued scenery, with a number of small crags, as evidenced by the relatively soft profiles of Blea Tarn Hill (168014), Birker Fell (175975) and Muncaster Fell (130988).

However, certain masses within the granite have withstood the power of the Eskdale glacier to remain as rocky hillocks in the valley floor, causing the stream to resort to a devious route. On the south flank of the valley, Gate Crag (186999) provides the last buttresses of the BVS before the sweep of the more rounded granite scenery on the horizon.

To illustrate that not all BVS country is craggy and wild, away on the western horizon the extremely smoothed outlines of Illgill Head (166049) and Whin Rigg (151035) seem to have escaped the gouging and plucking effects of the ice-sheets. This flank is in remarkable contrast to the northern face of the same fells when seen from Wastwater.

THE UPPER BASIN

The path leaves the road at the Brotherilkeld entrance (212012) and the first section around the farm is a flat valley floor with lateral moraines veneering the lower slopes and smoothed-and-plucked flanks up to the shoulder. Closer examination reveals several levels on this floor. At some stage in the late glacial period a lakelet was impounded behind a constriction below Wha House bridge. The sediments from this lake have been dissected by forerunners of the present Esk, and terraces remain.

Three such terraces are identifiable, the highest and hence the oldest being approximately 40ft above the present stream bed. This is the most fragmentary terrace abutting against the lateral moraine and screes. The second terrace is the most extensive and is criss-crossed by abandoned stream beds (incised perhaps 10ft.) Despite beds and lenses of finer gravel materials, the frequently coarse, rounded debris would suggest a vigorous stream with spate periods at snow-melt rather than a lake, with the exception of the uppermost terrace which is the floor-remnant of the late-glacial lakelet. The boulders are mainly BVS, although Eskdale Granite rubble appears below Brotherilkeld. The abundance of debris from the Eskdale Granite is one of its special features, the material being found not only locally but in drift down much of western England and into Wales. This seems to be due to the well-developed jointing systems, which aided the plucking action of the glaciers.

The north flanks show the last of the granite exposures, while the south flanks are crowned by lavas on Yew Crags, with their generally massive jointing systems. The valley floor is broken opposite Cowcove Beck (215022) by a hummocky ridge which is a combination of rock bar, moraine and post-glacial scree.

The resistant lava is seen beside the path and on this rests morainic debris, while to the south a fan of BVS scree is creeping outwards from Yew Crags. The band of hard rock can be seen continuing across the stream, here constricted and pushed to the northern side of the valley. Against the northern flank, between Cowcove Beck and the last field wall, is a series of morainic lobes which seem to be lateral moraines or the corner sections of a stage moraine.

Upstream to Bursting Gills (225030) the anticlinal axis following the line of the valley causes the beds to dip away on either flank, thus producing scarp crags, below which screes are steadily inundating the lower half of the valley. One angular lava block from Yew Crags sitting beside the path is more than 12ft long, while nearby in the stream bed is a partially rounded boulder of similar dimensions illustrating how even the largest material is slowly reduced by the weathering agents.

Above Bursting Gills the stream is working into solid rock, the stream gradient is greater, there is active incision, and a series of small waterfalls. The water-freshened surfaces of the boulders in the stream bed give the best opportunity to examine the local BVS, particularly at periods of low water. In addition to the grey

Fig 93: Throstle Garth Rock Steps

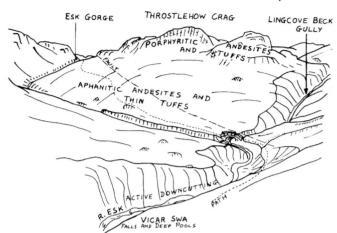

ESK GORGE   THROSTLEHOW CRAG   LINGCOVE BECK GULLY

PORPHYRITIC AND ANDESITES TUFFS

APHANITIC ANDESITES AND THIN TUFFS

FAULT

ACTIVE DOWNCUTTING   PATH

R. ESK   VICAR SWA FALLS AND DEEP POOLS

lavas ashes from fine to coarse are found, there are frequent examples of bedding, including gradations within individual beds, from coarse to fine ash.

At Vicar Swa (227036) the seasonally vigorous stream, with the aid of a considerable gradient, has cut a 30ft deep gorge (Figure 93) into the well-jointed lavas, the stream becoming a lovely alternation of crystal pool and sparkling fall.

At Throstle Garth the Esk and Lingcove Beck unite. They tumble down three massive steps through gorges and falls. The gorges follow master-joint systems and are incised as much as 70ft. The steps are the northerly dipping lava flows seen

from Border End, the northerly limit of the minor anticline along the Esk valley and on a larger scale, part of the southern limb of the Scafell syncline. The lavas are dark porphyritic and aphanitic flows with occasional vesicles of the Birker Fell Group. The top 10 to 15ft of some of the flows are flow-brecciated.

Climbing the path above the Esk gorge it is easy to imagine the mass of ice pouring over these lava flows, accentuating through time the steps we now see. The upslope sides of the rock-knobs exhibit fine examples of striations and polishing, while the downslope sides are plucked and craggy. Along the path, hornstones with a white surface patina indicate the proximity of a fault line, although there is less reddening by haematite staining than is common along such zones, eg the Rossett Gill shatter zone in upper Langdale (Chapter 5).

On the third step the stream flows across the ledge to find the lowest exit point, causing the two sharp bends in the stream course. In this ledge there was a lakelet, now evidenced by the flat marshy area of alluvium.

The topmost step begins the outcrop of the Airy's Bridge Group, which is composed mostly of more acid materials, particularly rhyolites and dacites. Above this particularly drift-masked uppermost step we emerge into the final basin below Scafell. This basin is floored by rock-knobs plastered with drift, between which are marshy hollows. This was an ice-collection basin and during the final stages of the glaciation masses of 'dead' ice melted in situ, leaving the hummocks of unsorted drift. There is a fine view of the sweep of the lava and tuff crags from Yeastyrigg Crags, past the Esk Hause col and across Great End to Scafell and Cam Spout. The paler acid materials of the Airy's Bridge Group underlie the basin and sweep up to Cam Spout Crag and Mickledore fault col. From Scafell itself, across to the Esk Hause col, the andesite tuffs and interbedded flows take over, to be followed by the youngest rocks, the Lingcomb Tarn Formation, on Broad Crag and Great End.

MIDDLE ESKDALE

Below the Wha bridge constriction, the floor widens but the flanks remain steep, with lateral moraines and roche moutonnées occurring intermittently as far as Eskdale Green along the northern side in particular. Immediately below the bridge granite blocks begin to appear in the walls and the BVS-granite junction crosses the valley floor at this point. However, the valley floor is filled with detritus and no junction is visible. From the Youth Hostel (196011), the valley floor becomes much more broken and a series of drift-plastered rocky eminences cross the floor, up to 75ft in height. The stream squeezes past to the south while the road wanders to the north.

This broken terrain can best be assimilated by taking the path signposted 'Footpath to Hardknott via Penny Hill' (189009). At the bridge there are good exposures of the pink granite in massive-jointed and water-smoothed blocks. Turn right beyond the bridge to Low Birker, with its splendid barn of granite and BVS blocks. Continue along the track to Force Beck (185002), and turn left upslope into Birker Force gorge. Here there is a series of waterfalls cut into the granite and at Birker Force itself (188999) the junction with the dark, hardened BVS andesites can be observed.

The flanks of Gate Crag provide a useful viewpoint for middle Eskdale (Figure 94). In the foreground the valley obstructions, with their asymmetrical shape, stand out – a long, smoothed upvalley side and an ice-plucked downvalley face. Before the improvements by man the hollows were marshy, hence the siting of Boot village and the farms just above the break of slope. Local variations in hardness and resistance, probably the result of less well-jointed zones in the granite, account for the survival of such rock prominences.

In the middle distance the slopes are broken by the very considerable valley of Whillan Beck, and the red spoil-heaps of the disused Boot haematite mines. The subdued granite topography is evident in the contrast between the rounded spurs from Muncaster to Birdhow, and the craggy BVS in the upper valley. In detail, patches of BVS form crags at Great Barrow (185018) and Blea Tarn Hill (168014). These are remnants of the roof rocks over the granite stock (Figure 95A), and this is an opportune point at which to consider the nature of the intrusion and the resultant rock type.

The injection of liquid magma at great pressure and temperatures into pre-existing rock involves the

Fig 94: Middle Eskdale Above Boot Village

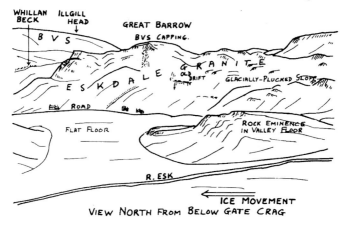

VIEW NORTH FROM BELOW GATE CRAG

Fig 95: The Granitic Stock Underlying Middle Eskdale

A

SCHEMATIC IMPRESSION OF ESKDALE—TYPE INTRUSION

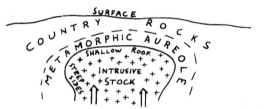

B

two principal processes of forcing aside the rocks to gain entrance, and the chemical absorption and replacement of the 'country' rock by the igneous material. Such emplacements are usually associated with periods of crustal movement and mountain building. The Eskdale and other major intrusions of the Lake District are believed to be Devonian in age, some 400 million years ago and towards the end of the Caledonian orogeny.

There are many forms of intrusion depending upon such factors as the nature of the pre-existing rock and structures, the length of time and persistence of the intrusion. The Eskdale granite intrusion is a relatively simple structure now exposed over more

than thirty-five square miles, making it the largest of the Lake District intrusions. It occurred in two main stages, the first, a more basic stage, producing a grey or bluish rock more a granodiorite than a true granite. This earlier type occupies the western sector from the south of Muncaster Fell to the southern limit beyond Kinmont Beck, forming the belt of beautifully rounded hills rising from the coastal plain immediately east of the A595.

The second, more highly acid stage, produced the true pink granite. This is a rose-pink to brownish-pink rock, at first glance comparable with Shap Granite but lacking the long felspar crystals. It has a medium-to-coarse texture, almost brick-like in appearance, with some square cleavage and an irregularly spaced, usually rectangular jointing system. The constituents are dominated by perthite (58 per cent in a typical specimen) and quartz (32 per cent) making this a highly acid rock. It can be examined in the stream bed near Boot, or in the walls of Beckfoot Quarry (168006), or in the enormously thick walls around Boot village. As with the Ennerdale Granophyre, the jointing system aids the production of copious debris.

The so-called 'grey granite' of the western sector is less acid, being a granodiorite, with a markedly different mineral makeup from the pink granite: quartz (27 per cent), orthoclase felspar (23 per cent), perthite (20 per cent) and plagioclase felspar (12 per cent). The rock is grey and coarse-grained, with the darker micas standing out. The jointing is again variable and is best seen in the Waberthwaite Quarries (113944) south of Eskdale where it was quarried for monuments, kerbstones and later, road base. Both rock types have suffered noticeable alteration, shown particularly by the development of chlorite and sericite.

Typical of igneous intrusions, there are variations, eg the greenish patches seen in the northern sector of the outcrop between Eel Tarn (189019) and Great How (198041). In addition there are variations near the margins where a finer-grained, very acid pink type is sometimes observable, eg below Gate Crag. Finally, although the intrusion was in essence a two-stage event, the granodiorite followed by the granite, there was a final dying stage when dikes (usually felsite, quartz porphyry or aplite, ie highly acid materials) were injected through the stock with a common trend rather west of north. Today they can be identified by their coarse graining and their resistance to erosion, which causes them to stand out as ridges, eg quartz porphyries some 50 yards wide run across the otherwise-smooth slopes of Whin Rigg. Such dike systems are common as the last spasms of activity in the injection of plutonic masses, eg the aplite dikes of the Shap intrusion.

The two-stage intrusion is in the form known as a 'stock' (Figure 95B), with a fairly flat roof and steep sides. In some localities the junction can be seen and plotted, as on Great Barrow, but elsewhere it is hidden by drift, scree etc. When the actual junction is hidden, it is often possible to locate its approximate position by changes in the rocks near to the junction.

Close to the granite, where the metamorphism has been most severe, the andesites assume a purplish hue with a baked appearance and are rather brittle. The innermost zone, up to two miles wide, is characterised by the dark mineral biotite. Beyond this zone epidote and hornblende, again dark minerals, become more common, to be succeeded outwards by a chloritic zone in which metamorphism has been slight.

Boot village sits below the crags into which the adits of Nab Bill haematite mine were driven (176015). Specimens of haematite are easily obtainable from the purplish-red spoil-heaps alongside the old rail trackway up the slope directly behind the village. The mine operated from 1870 until 1912, the ore being taken out by a railway to Ravenglass. This is the track which has been reconstructed as a tourist line to Dalegarth (173008). The origin of the Lake District iron ores has been a subject of much controversy. Some occur in the Carboniferous Limestones fringing the massif and are replacements in the sedimentary strata. The Boot haematites are found near the roof of the granite stock and seem to be concentrates as the result of percolation from the overlying BVS.

If time permits, continue to Blea Tarn Hill (169014). This is a good example of the subdued granite country, with intermittent drift and also has the poorly-exposed patch of BVS sitting on the granite. A better locality for observing the granite/BVS junction, and the contrasting topography developed upon the two rock types, is around the shallow rock basin of Devoke Water (160970). Further points of interest are the variations in the granite character seen along the north shore of the lake, and the ice-scoured uplands on the approach from the Ulpha road.

LOWER ESKDALE

The topographic features of interest in lower Eskdale below Eskdale Green are connected principally with the Pleistocene glaciation. The pre-glacial scenery would have shown the alignments as today, with a river valley flanked on the south by the hills around Devoke Water and on the north by the Muncaster Fell granite ridge, separated from the main hill mass by the Eskdale Green gap.

At maximum glaciation the Lake District ice-sheet inundated the whole area and moved generally westwards before being diverted southwards across Muncaster Fell by the powerful Irish Sea ice-mass, eg the presence of glacial drift at above 1,60ft on the fells above Wastwater. As the Main Glaciation waned, bringing lower ice levels, tongues of ice moved down Eskdale and Miterdale, and in time Muncaster began to emerge as a nunatak.

Fig 96: Classical Meltwater Channel Hypothesis

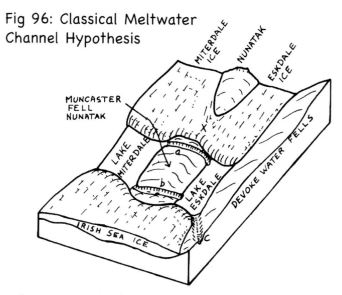

SCHEMATIC IMPRESSION OF THE GLACIAL LAKES AND CHANNELS IN LOWER ESKDALE

The Irish Sea ice continued to press eastwards as is evidenced by fragments of St Bees Sandstone and Skiddaw Slate in ground moraines and gravels as far upvalley as Eskdale Green, well to the east of the outcrops of these rock types.

The classical interpretation of deglaciation has been based upon a succession of retreating ice-fronts along which developed marginal meltwater channels whose waters flowed into pre-glacial lakes impounded between rock and ice. As in Figure 96 a portion of

Muncaster Fell is exposed as a nunatak separating the two lakes with Eskdale Green col (x) still covered by ice. Two meltwater channels (a and b) are being cut across the lowest points of the ridge, the waters flowing south into the lower lake in Eskdale where deltas are being formed. This lake is itself drained via a marginal channel across Stainton Fell (c).

Through time the ice-fronts retreat and the lakes are able to seek lower outlets, thereby abandoning the earlier higher channels. The

Fig 97: Muncaster Fell Meltwater Channels

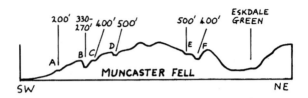

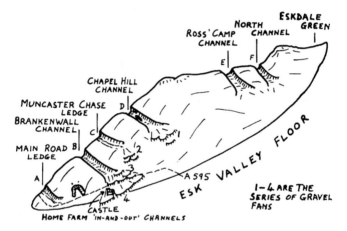

results of such an interpretation are a chronological succession of marginal meltwater channels and their associated deposits (Figure 97). Muncaster Fell is indeed crossed by a series of channels some of which have deposits below their southern exits. But despite the beautiful logic of such an explanation, modern geomorphologists tell us first that ice-sheets often downwaste and melt in situ, and second that much of the meltwaters flow on, within or below the ice rather than marginal to it. According to this latter hypothesis, these Muncaster channels were formed subglacially and not necessarily in sequence according to their altitude, although it is possible that the higher notches, eg Ross's Camp (125991) and Chapel Hill (106978) channels, may have been 'superimposed' on to the ridge as it emerged as a nunatak by sections of supra- or englacial streams flowing on to the freshly-exposed rock. Thus ice would replace lakes Miterdale and Eskdale on Figure 96.

When examined closely, these Muncaster Fell channels are seen to be best developed on the southern flank, falling away fairly steeply. The overlapping fans, resembling fish scales, are not true deltas but the result of deposition in cavities and tunnels beneath the ice. Such an origin would help to explain the absence of exit deposits below some channels, the postulation being that any such gravels were deposited upon or within the ice and later dispersed as the ice disappeared.

Two other forms of subglacial channel can be seen at the western end of the ridge. The first, shown as the Muncaster Chase Ledge (103971) and Main Road Ledge (091967) on Figure 97, are benches cut by meltwaters, one flank of whose channel was cut into the ice. The second type, the Home Farm 'in-and-out' channel (096968), marks the section where a sub or englacial stream impinged upon the rock slope, returning to the ice. After the disappearance of the ice, these incomplete and disconnected channels remain in the hillside.

The five main channels and their deposits can be examined by a traverse of Muncaster Fell beginning in the castle grounds,

which have been landscaped largely upon the sub-ice gravels below the exit to the Brankenwall Channel between the 200ft and 100ft contours (4 on Figure 97). The top surfaces are gently lobate but end abruptly to the south at an ice-contact slope. This edge has provided an excellent site for a terrace, which yields a famous view up Eskdale to the Scafell range. (The castle and grounds are open to the public.)

The gravels incline north of the A595 to an upper set above 200ft around the mouth of the Brankenwall ravine beside the farm (099970). This channel is a two-stage trough with a more open upper section beginning at approximately 360ft OD, and a lower V-shaped gash which plunges to 270ft. Although today forested and obscured, this has clearly been cut by a vigorous torrent capable of transporting the considerable materials needed to build up the gravel fans. A track leads into this channel from the road junction at the vicarage (100968), but the main track of the traverse passes NE from this junction. After about 400 yards it leads past the Muncaster Chase ledge exit, while to the south lie further lobes of sub-ice gravels.

The large Chapel Hill channel is partly obscured by an artificial tarn, but its bevelled sides identify it as a typical meltwater channel,

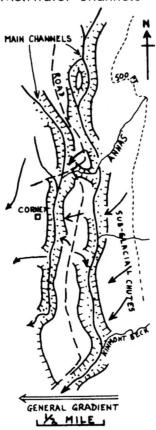

Fig 98:
The Corney-Kinmont
Meltwater Channels

while the gill which flows from the tarn has dissected the highest set of gravels, from 400ft to 200ft OD, across which the path runs through the wood. It continues along the ridge summit with a number of Eskdale Granite exposures, and giving good views of Eskdale and Miterdale whose flat floors suggest that although the long-standing pro-glacial lakes may now be discounted, at some stage temporary lakes lay in the valleys yielding the sediments of the flat floors. A number of rock-knobs in Miterdale would have stood out as islands. The descent of the northern section of the ridge crosses the Ross Camp and North Channels, both with bevelled sides and flat floors although without exit gravels. The absence of meltwater channels through the Eskdale Green col exemplifies the presence of stagnant ice-masses melting in situ, with any meltwaters crossing the gap doing so in supr- aor englacial streams.

The return walk from Muncaster Head (140990) via Chapel's Monument (110975) follows the lower ground and gives views of the sub-ice gravels from a different angle, revealing how they grade down from the channel exits.

The meltwaters continued to drain southwards, across or beneath the ice banked up against the Waberthwaite Fells. These waters cut a series of benches and channels in the flanks of the fell, particularly between Barnscar (130960) and Kinmont (118898) (Figure 98). The two main channels run N-S upslope of the A595 on either side of the lane which joins the fell farms. The channels range up to 100 yards in width and are frequently marshy. They were once believed to be ice-marginal but are clearly subglacial, possessing the tell-tale characteristics of occasionally reversed gradients (the sub-ice waters, under pressure, being capable of flowing upslope), of being joined by short cross-cut channels (Figure 98), and of sudden changes of direction, particularly sharp, steeper downslope sections where the channels turned downslope beneath the ice. In addition there are several subglacial chutes upslope of the main channel. These are short steep-sided valleys, somewhat oblique to the slope, beginning and ending abruptly, and sometimes joining the main channels. They were formed by waters rushing downslope beneath the ice and gouging these chutes. In the Kinmont Beck valley floor below Buckbarrow Bridge (134902) and east of High Corney (125928), there are eskers, low sinuous ridges formed in the ice tunnels.

Glossary and Abbreviations

ABLATION – Evaporation and melting of the surface of ice.

ACID – Applied to an igneous rock more than 66 per cent of whose mass is composed of silica. Usually oversaturated with silica so that free silica in the form of quartz is visible.

AGGLOMERATE – A mass of large rock fragments mixed with finer material, most usually with reference to rocks produced as the result of explosive volcanic action.

AMPHIBOLE – A family of rock-forming minerals, mainly silicates of magnesium, calcium and iron. Hornblende is the most common member.

APLITE – A very fine – grained acid microgranite made up almost entirely of quartz and felspar. Usually pink and found in veins in the parent granite.

ARENACEOUS – Applied to rocks of a sandy nature.

ARÊTE – A narrow, sharp mountain ridge most typically found between two corries or glacial troughs.

ARGILLACEOUS – Applied to rocks of a clay nature.

BARYTES – Barium sulphate: a white, rather heavy mineral, usually found in veins in massive crystalline form, perhaps in association with lead and fluorspar.

BASE-LEVEL – The level below which a land surface cannot be reduced by running water.

BASIC – Applied to igneous rocks with a silica content of less than 55 per cent, eg basalt, dolerite, gabbro.

BATHOLITH – A large dome – shaped igneous intrusive mass at least 100 sq km in areal exposure and usually of granite.

BERGSCHRUND – The wide crevasse or series of crevasses found between the rock wall of a corrie and the mass of ice which occupies it.

BOULDER CLAY – Material deposited by ice-sheets. It is usually fine clay containing considerable amounts of pebbles and boulders of all sizes.

BP – Standard geological abbreviation for 'before the present' and used for dating purposes.

BVS – Standard abbreviation for the 'Borrowdale Volcanic Series' of Ordovician age.

CHLORITE – A silicate of iron, magnesium and aluminium with hydroxyl. Usually greenish and occurring commonly in igneous rocks as a secondary mineral from the alteration of biotite or hornblende. Also common in metamorphic rocks.

CLASTIC – Applied to rocks composed of the broken fragments of other rocks.

CLEAVAGE – The way certain fine-grained rocks split. Produced by dynamic metamorphism which causes flakes of micaceous minerals to align themselves at right-angles to the direction of pressure.

COMPETENCE – The relative strength of rock when subjected to folding.

CONGLOMERATE – A rock consisting of rounded pebbles in a finer matrix and usually with some natural cementing material to consolidate it.

CORRIE, CIRQUE, CWM – An amphitheatre usually associated with the head of a mountain valley and caused by the action of ice.

DACITE – An igneous rock of quartz-andesite. The fine-grained equivalent of granodiorite.

DIASTROPHISM – A general term for the action of forces which have deformed the earth's crust.

DIKE – An igneous intrusion where molten material ascended a near-vertical fissure to solidify as a wall of rock at a high angle to any bedding.

DIORITE – An intermediate plutonic igneous rock (silica content 55 – 66 per cent).

DOLERITE – A hypabyssal igneous rock; basic, of medium grain and composed essentially of calcic plagioclase felspars and pyroxene often with olivine.

DRUMLIN – A smooth cigar-shaped mound of glacial drift, moulded by the moving ice-sheet. May have a rock core.

ENDOGENETIC – Geological processes originating within the earth and rocks, ore deposits and landforms which owe their origin to such processes.

ENDOMORPHIC – Those phases of contact metamorphism that are developed in the intrusion itself.

ENGLACIAL – Embedded within or moving within a glacier.

ERRATIC – A boulder transported by an ice-sheet or glacier which has since disappeared.

ESKER – A long, often sinuous ridge of sand and gravel laid down by a river beneath a glacier.

FACIES – In general, the appearance and character of individual beds or homogeneous series of beds, but may be used by geologists in a wide variety of senses.

FAULT – A fracture or break in a rock series along which there has been vertical or lateral movement or both.

FELSITE – A very fine-grained rock composed mainly of quartz and felspar. Individual crystals not visible to the naked eye.

FELSPAR – The principal family of rock-forming minerals, silicates of aluminium and a variety of potassium, sodium, calcium. Main groups are orthoclase (potassium) and plagioclase (sodium).

FLAG – Sandstone or sandy limestone rocks, usually containing mica, which are fissile along the bedding planes and split into slabs.

FLUORSPAR – Calcium fluoride or fluorite, occurring as a vein mineral and formerly used in lead smelting.

FLUVIO-GLACIAL – Produced by streams resulting from the melting of glacier ice.

GABBRO – The plutonic variety of basic igneous rock, ie silica less than 55 per cent. Usually coarse-grained and dark in colour.

GALENA – Lead sulphide (PbS). A grey mineral with a shining metallic lustre, relatively soft and very heavy with cubic crystals. A vein mineral and the principal ore of lead.

GEANTICLINE – A very large anticline.

GEOSYNCLINE – A very large syncline or downwarping of the earth's crust.

GRANITE – The most common of plutonic igneous rocks. Coarse-grained, acid, sometimes porphyritic and consists essentially of quartz, felspar, micas and hornblende.

GREYWACKE – A coarse-grained clastic sedimentary rock, frequently containing much felspar among its grains.

GRIT – A coarse-grained clastic sedimentary rock composed of quartz grains, often with siliceous cement.

HORIZON – A plane of stratification in sedimentary rocks. Assumed to have been once horizontal and continuous.

HORNBLENDE – A member of the amphibole family. Common in metamorphic rocks and in igneous rocks as dark horny-looking crystals. Contains magnesium, iron, aluminium, calcium.

HORNFELS – A hard fine-grained rock produced by thermal metamorphism of argillaceous rocks. Most common constituents are quartz, felspar, mica.

HORST – An uplifted block of country bounded by faults.

HYDROTHERMAL – Pertaining to hot water with respect to its action in producing mineral changes in rocks. Particularly associated with emanations from magmatic intrusions where hot water and gases are injected through the surrounding country rock.

IGNEOUS – Applied to rocks which originated from the cooling and solidifica tion of molten magma.

IGNIMBRITE – An ash-flow pyroclastic rock formed from a nuée ardente. Typically a tuff, welded at the time of deposition by coalescence of the glass fragments..

IMBRICATE – Where small sections of rock have been thrust by faulting one over another, rather like the tiles of a roof.

INLIER – An outcrop of older rocks entirely surrounded by rocks younger in age.

JOINT – A surface or fissure in a rock following a dominant direction along which there has been minimal displacement. A rock may possess several jointing systems which influence the form of its fragmentation.

KAME – A mound of fluvio-glacial material laid down by waters marginal to glaciers and ice-sheets and originally banked against the ice.

KAOLINISATION – The process by which the felspars of granites are altered by heated gases and waters into kaolin or china clay.

LACCOLITH – An igneous intrusion in the form of a low dome with flat base intruded among sedimentary rocks which themselves become domed by the force of the intruded magma.

LAMPROPHYRE – A basic igneous rock rich in porphyritic crystals of biotite in a groundmass of alkali felspar. Frequently a dike material.

LITHOLOGY – The physical structure of a rock, its structure, grain size etc.

MAGMA – The molten material of the lower crust and upper mantle of the earth from which igneous rocks solidify.

METAMORPHIC AUREOLE – The zone of metamorphosed rocks around an igneous intrusion, the degree of metamorphism decreasing away from the intrusion.

METAMORPHISM – The transformation of a rock through the application of heat and/or pressure to produce a new texture and, if sufficiently severe, recrystalisation, ie a process of change without the introduction of new material.

METASOMATISM – Processes by which one mineral is replaced by another of different chemical composition owing to reactions set up by the introduction of materials from external sources, eg by the percolation of water containing minerals in solution.

MICA – A family of rock-forming minerals, silicates of aluminium, potassium and often magnesium and iron in the dark micas, all having hydroxyl (OH). They have perfect cleavage and split into distinctive plates with a lustrous surface.

MINERALISER – Magmatic gases such as hydrogen, water and compounds of fluorine, sulphur and other volatile substances which facilitate recrystallisation of many minerals, help in the formation of new minerals and help to concentrate metallic compounds into masses of economic potential.

MISFIT – A stream too small to have cut the valley through which it flows.

MORAINE – Rock material having been carried and deposited by a glacier. Includes unsorted material of all sizes.

NUÉE ARDENTE – An incandescent cloud of gas and fragments which may form part of the eruption of an acid volcano. Moves at high speeds, close to the ground.

NUNATAK – A rock mass projecting above an ice – sheet or glacier.

OUVINE – A family of rock-forming minerals, silicates of magnesium and iron. Olive-green and glassy in appearance and common in basic igneous rocks.

OROGENY – A period of mountain building.

PERIGLACIAL – Applied to environments adjacent to glaciers.

PERTHITE – A mineral resulting from crystal intergrowth of potassium and sodium felspar.

PHENOCRYST – Large crystal within a groundmass in igneous rocks.

PLUMBAGO OR GRAPHITE – Almost pure carbon; a black soft material.

PLUTONIC – Applied to igneous rocks which solidified at great depth below the surface.

PNEUMATOLYSIS – The process whereby minerals are produced from volatile compounds within the magmatic gases known as mineralisers, given off particularly during the final stages of the cooling of a magmatic mass.

PORPHYRITIC – A rock texture in which the crystals of one mineral constituent are embedded within a groundmass of finer grain.

PYROCLAST – Fragmental materials thrown out by the explosive action of a volcano.

QUARTZ – The most common crystalline silica and a very hard glassy-looking mineral, often occurring in the hexagonal form.

RANDKLUFT – The space between the ice and the headwall in a corrie down which meltwater may flow.

REJUVENATION – The result of land uplift renewing erosional activity by streams.

RHYOLITE – Silica-rich, acid lava; the fine grained equivalent of a granite.

RUDACEOUS – Applied to rocks of a pebbly and stony nature.

SATURATED – Minerals within igneous rocks which are capable of forming in the presence of free silica.

SHALE – An argillaceous clastic sedimentary rock.

SILICA – Silicon dioxide, occurring mainly as the mineral quartz.

SILL – An igneous sheet intrusion injected between the bedding planes of pre-existing rocks.

SLATE – A metamorphosed argillaceous rock produced especially from a shale. Various degrees of metamorphism are found.

SPHERULITE – A small spherical mass of radiating fibrous crystals, often with concentric banding, found in igneous rocks.

STOCK – Small igneous intrusion, similar in form to a batholith but covering only a few square miles or less.

SUBGLACIAL – Refers to movements, materials or processes beneath an ice-mass.

SUPRAGLACIAL – Refers to movements, materials or processes on the upper surface of an ice-mass.

TECTONIC – Refers to the structure in a rock or geologic unit.

THRUST – A low-angled reverse fault.

TILL – Boulder-clay, but emphasising the stiff, impervious clay component and not the stone content of this form of glacial drift which originates beneath a glacier or ice-sheet.

TUFF – The rock resulting from deposition and consolidation of fine- to medium-grained volcanic ash.

UNCONFORMITY – A discontinuity between two rock types denoting a break in the depositional sequence.

VESICULAR – Igneous rocks containing gas holes.

Appendix

Geological Time Scale

(after A. HOLMES, *Principles of Physical Geology*)

Era	Period and system	Time of beginning (million years BP)	Duration (million years)
	Quaternary		
	Recent (Holocene)		
	Glacial (Pleistocene)	2	2
	Tertiary		
Cainozoic	Pliocene	12	10
	Miocene	25	13
	Oligocene	40	15
	Eocene	60	20
	Palaeocene	70	10
	Cretaceous	135	65
Mesozoic	Jurassic	180	45
	Triassic	225	45
	Upper Palaeozoic		
	Permian	270	45
	Carboniferous	350	80
	Devonian	400	50
Palaeozoic	Lower Palaeozoic		
	Silurian	440	40
	Ordovician	500	60
	Cambrian	600	100
Precambrian	Proterozoic Eozoic	up to 4,500	up to 4,000

Bibliography and References

GENERAL REFERENCES OF INTEREST

British Palaeozoic Fossils (British Museum, Natural History, 1966)

Challinor, J. *A Dictionary of Geology* (University of Wisconsin Press, 3rd ed 1967)

Himus, G. W. and Sweeting, M. M. *Elements of Field Geology* (University Tutorial Press, 1972)

Kirkaldy, J. F. *Fossils in Colour* (Blandford, 1970)

Millward, R. and Robinson, A. **The Lake District** (Eyre & Spottiswoode, 1970) *Cumbria* (Macmillan, 1972)

Open University, Geology, Blocks 1-6 (Course S23, Science 1972)

Pearsall, W. H. *Lake District National Park Guide* (HMSO, 1969)

Shackleton, E. H. *Lakeland Geology* (Dalesman, 3rd ed 1971)

Taylor, B. J. et al. *British Regional Geology: Northern England* (HMSO, 4th ed 1971)

SELECTED LIST OF USEFUL REFERENCES

Blackie, R. C. *'The Silurian Rocks of the Kentmere District, Westmorland'*, Proc Liverpool Geol Soc, 16 (1933), 88-105

Brown, P. E., Miller, J. A. and Soper, N. J. *'Age of the Principal Intrusions of the Lake District'*, Proc Yorks Geol Soc, 34 (1963-4), 331-42

Clark, L. *'The Borrowdale Volcanic Series between Buttermere and Wasdale, Cumberland'*, Proc Yorks Geol Soc, 34 (1963-4), 343-56

Dakyns, J. R., Tiddeman, R. H. and Goodchild, J. G. *'The Geology of the Country between Appleby, Ullswater and Haweswater'*, Mem Geol Survey, 6 (1897)

Dixon, E. E. L. *'The Retreat of the Lake District Ice-cap in the Ennerdale Area, West Cumberland'*, Summ Prog Geol Survey (1921), 118-28

Eastwood, T., Dixon, E. E. L., Hollingworth, S. E. and Smith, B.

'The Geology of the Whitehaven and Workington District', Mem Geol Survey (HMSO, 1931)

Elles, G. L. *'The Graptolite Fauna of the Skiddaw Slates'*, QJGS, 54 (1898), 463-539

Ewart, A. *'Hydrothermal Alteration in the Carrock Fell Area, Cumberland'*. Geol Mag, 99 (1962), 1-8

Firman, R. J. *'The Borrowdale Volcanic Series between Wastwater and Duddon Valley, Cumberland'*, Proc Yorks Geol Soc, 31 (1957-8),39-64

Grantham, D. R. *'The Petrology of the Shap Granite'*, Proc Geol Ass, 39 (1928), 299-331

Green, J. F. N. *'The Structure of the Eastern Part of the Lake District'*, Proc Geol Ass, 26 (1915), 195-223

– *'The Age of the Chief Intrusions of the Lake District'*, Proc Geol Ass, 28 (1917), 1-30

– *'The Mell Fell Conglomerate'*, Proc Geol Ass, 29 (1918), 117-25

– *'The Skiddaw Granite: A Structural Study'*, Proc Geol Ass, 29 (1918), 126-36

– *'The Vulcanicity of the Lake District'*, Proc Geol Ass, 30 (1919), 153-82

– *'The Geological Structure of the Lake District'*, Proc Geol Ass, 31 (1920), 109-26

Gresswell, R. K. *'The Glacial Geomorphology of the South-eastern Part of the Lake District'*, Liverpool and Manchester Geol J, 1 (1952),57-70

– *'The Glaciology of the Coniston Basin'*, Liverpool and Manchester Geol J, 3 (1962), 83-95

Hancox, E. J. *'The Haweswater Dolerite, Westmorland'*, Proc Liverpool Geol Soc, 16 (1934), 173-97

Harker, A. and Marr, J. E. *'The Shap Granite and Associated Rocks'*, QJGS, 47 (1891), 266-328

Hartley, J. J. *'The Succession and Structure of the Borrowdale Volcanic Series as Developed in the Area Lying between the Lakes of Grasmere,*

Windermere and Coniston', Proc Geol Ass, 36 (1925), 203-26

– '*Volcanic and Other Igneous Rocks of Great and Little Langdale'*, Proc Geol Ass, 43 (1932), 32-69

Hay, T. '*The Glaciology of the Ullswater Area'*, Geog J, 84 (1934), 136

– '*Rosthwaite Moraines and Other Lakeland Notes'*, Geog J, 103 (1944), 119-24

Helm, D. G. and Roberts, B. '*The Relationship between the Skiddaw and Borrowdale Volcanic Groups in the English Lake District'*, Nature, 232 (1971), 181-3

Hitchen, C. S. '*The Skiddaw Granite and its Residual Products'*, QJGS, 90 (1934), 158-200

Hollingworth, S. E. '*The Geology of the Lake District: a Review'*, Proc Geol Ass, 65 (1955), 385-402

Huddart, D. '*Deglaciation in the Ennerdale Area: a Reinterpretation'*, Proc Cumb Geol Soc, 2 (1967), 63-75

Jackson, D. E. '*Geology of the Skiddaw Slates between the Buttermere Valley and Troutbeck, Cumberland'*, unpublished PhD thesis, King's College, University of Durham (1956)

– '*Stratigraphy of the Skiddaw Group between Buttermere and Mungrisdale, Cumberland'*, Geol Mag, 98 (1961), 515-28

Manley, G. '*The Late-glacial Climate of Northwest England'*, Liverpool and Manchester Geol J, 2 (1958-61), 188-215

Marr, J. E. and Nicholson, H. A. '*The Stockdale Shales'*, QJGS, 44 (1888), 654-732

The Geology of the Lake District (CUP, 1916)

Miller, A. A. '*Pre-glacial Erosion Surfaces around the Irish Sea Basin'*, Proc Yorks Geol Soc, 24 (1939), 31-59

Mitchell, G. H. '*The Succession and Structure of the Borrowdale Volcanic Series of Troutbeck, Kentmere and the Western Part of Long Sleddale, Westmorland'*, QJGS, 85 (1929), 9-44

– 'The Geomorphology of the Eastern Part of the Lake District', Proc Liverpool Geol Soc, 15 (1931), 322-38

– 'The Borrowdale Volcanic Series of the Country between Long Sleddale and Shap', QJGS, 90 (1934), 418-44

– 'The Geological History of the Lake District', Proc Yorks Geol Soc, 30 (1956), 407-63

– 'The BV Rocks of the Seathwaite Fells, Lancashire', Liverpool and Manchester Geol J, 3 (1962-3), 289-300

Moseley, F. 'The Succession and StructUre of the Borrowdale Volcanic Rocks Southeast of Ullswater', QJGS, 116 (1960), 55-84

– 'The Succession and Structure of the Borrowdale Volcanic Rocks Northwest of Ullswater', Geol J, 4 (1964), 127-42

– 'A Tectonic History of Northwest England', QJGS, 128 (1972), 561-98

Oliver, R. L. 'The Borrowdale Volcanic Series and Associated Rocks of the Scafell area, Lake District', QJGS, 117 (1961), 377-417

Parry, G. T. 'The Erosion Surfaces of the Southwestern Lake District', Trans IBG, No 28 (1960), 39-54

Postlethwaite, J. Mines and Mining in the Lake District, (Moxon, Leeds, 1889)

Raistrick, A. 'The Glaciation of Borrowdale', ProcYorks Geol Soc, 29 (1925), 155-81

Rastall, R. H. 'The Buttermere and Ennerdale Granophyre', QJGS, 62 (1906), 253-74

– 'The Skiddaw Granite and its Metamorphism', QJGS, 66 (1910), 116

Reade, T. M. 'Eskdale Drift and its Bearing on Glacial Geology', Geol Mag, 10 (1893), 9-20

Roberts, D. E. 'Structures of the Skiddaw Slates in the Caldew Valley, Cumberland', Geol J, 7 (1971), 225-38

Rose, W. C. C. 'The Sequence and Structure of the Skiddaw Slates in the Keswick-Buttermere Area', Proc Geol Ass, 65 (1955), 403-6

Scrivener, J. B. *'The Grainsgill Greisen of Carrock Fell'*, Geol Mag, 3 (1916), 239-40

Simpson, A. *'The Stratigraphy and Tectonics of the Skiddaw Slates and the Relationship of the Overlying Borrowdale Volcanic Series in Part of the Lake District'*, Geol J, 5 (1967), 391-418

Simpson, B. *'The Glacier Lakes of Eskdale, Miterdale and Wasdale, Cumberland, and the Retreat of the Ice during the Main Glaciation'*, QJGS, 88 (1932), 57-83

– *'The Petrology of the Eskdale Granite'*, Proc Geol Ass, 45 (1934), 17-34

Smith, R. A. *'The Deglaciation of Southwestern Cumberland'*, Proc Cumb Geol Soc, 2 (1967), 76-83

– *A bibliography of Lake District geology and geomorphology* (Keswick, Cumb Geol Soc, 1969)

Trotter, F. M. *'The Age of the Ore Deposits of the Lake District and of the Alston Block'*, Geol Mag, 76 (1944), 223-9

Trotter, F. M. and Hollingworth, S. E. *'The Glacial Sequence in the North of England'*, Geol Mag, 69 (1932), 374-80

Walker, D. *'The Glaciation of the Langdale Fells'*, GeolJ, 5 (1966)

Ward, J. C. *'The Geology of the Northern Part of the English Lake District'*, Mem Geol Survey, 12 (HMSO, 1876)

The author dedicated this book to Andrew Morrall
for his love of the countryside

Index